Dr. Chuck Missler

LEARN THE BIBLE *in* 24 HOURS®

COMPREHENSIVE WORKBOOK

KH

Learn the Bible in 24 Hours

Comprehensive Workbook

Dedicated to Dr. Harold Wilson
February 7, 1941 - August 9, 2004

P.O. Box D, Coeur d'Alene, Idaho 83816-0347 1-800-546-8731

How to Use this Workbook

This workbook is not required for successful completion of Koinonia Institute classes. It can be a beneficial study guide for students who wish to use it. The workbook is designed to give structure to individual and small group Bible studies.

For maximum benefit, please read the following tips:

1. Before starting each session, please read through the study questions and, if part of a small group, the discussion questions that pertain to that session.

2. The first section of each session is designed to help you take notes. You will discover that there is much more information than space provided, so it may be helpful to have extra paper on which to write.

3. If you are a small group leader, please feel free to use the questions at the back of the workbook to facilitate discussion within your group. See the *Discussion Questions for Small Group Leaders* section.

4. If you are interested in taking these courses online as part of a structured study through Koinonia Institute, please go to www.studycenter.com to sign up. (There are special offers available for small groups who wish to take classes together as a group.) If you wish to receive college credit, we invite you to visit www.studycenter.com/degrees.html

5. For more information on Koinonia Institute, please download the free KI Handbook at www.studycenter.com. See also the back page of this workbook for a brief overview.

Learn the Bible
in 24 Hours
Hour One
Introduction

What's Ahead:

- The Ultimate Literary Adventure
- The Cosmic War
- The Ultimate Personal Adventure
  - –The Miracle of our Origin
  - –The Mystery of our Destiny
  - –The Urgency of Participation
    - **–Our Unique Advantage**
      - »Two Basic Discoveries

Two Critical Discoveries

1) We have in our possession an *Integrated* Message System
   - –66 separate books
   - –Penned by 40 different individuals
   - –Over thousands of years
2) Which provably has its origin from *outside our time domain.*

A Few Caveats

- The Word of God is *Inexhaustible.*
  - 24 *years* would be insufficient…
- The truth is in the details.
  - Every detail is connected to every other.
- Our Goal: A Strategic Grasp of the Total
  - A conceptual grounding in the major truths
  - A navigational awareness to fit it all together

Collapse of Skeptical Theories

- Historicity of Patriarchal accounts
- Denial of writing in Moses' day
- Gospels and Epistles: 2nd century?

Refuted by:

- Archaeological discoveries
- Documentary discoveries
- Competent analysis

Some Preliminaries

- Shedding the baggage of our misconceptions
- 20th century science has vindicated the Biblical perspectives of reality
  - The Finite Universe
  - The Discovery of the nature of Time
  - The realization of Hyperspaces

Trigonometry

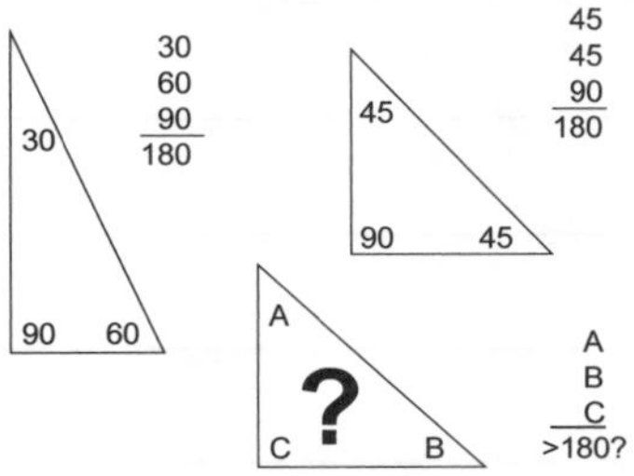

Einstein's Revolution

Special Relativity (1905)

- Length, mass, velocity and time are *relative* to velocity of the observers

General Relativity (1915)

- No distinction between time & space
  = a 4-dimensional continuum
  (Confirmed 12 ways to 19 decimals)

Demonstrations

- Atomic Clocks
  Faster by 10^{-16} /meter
- Aircraft experiment (1971)
  Eastward : lost 0.059 microsec.
  Westward: gained 0.273 microsec.
- Twin Astronauts (hypothetical)
  Alpha Centauri trip

Time is *not* uniform

- Time is a *physical* property
- Time *varies* with
  - Mass
  - Acceleration
  - Gravity

  …among other things…
- We exist in *more* than 3 dimensions
  - Apparently, 10…

The Geometry of Eternity

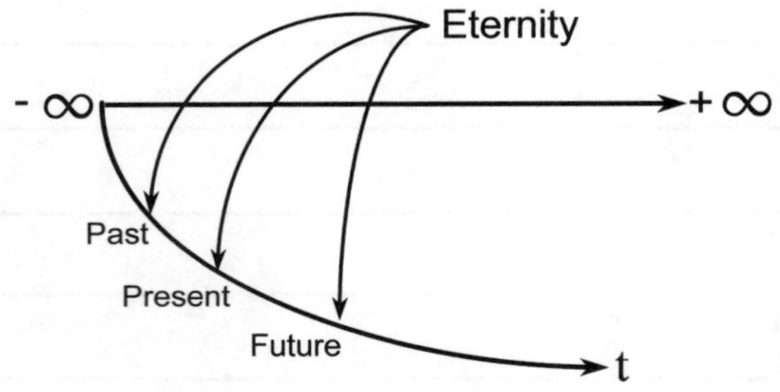

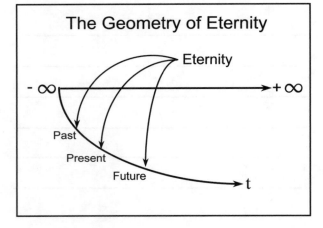

Dimensions of "Reality"

- Nachmonides, (12th Century)
  - 10 dimensions
    - only 4 are "knowable"

Commentary on Genesis, 1263

- Particle Physicists, (20th Century)
  - 10 dimensions
    - 4 are directly measurable: (3 spatial + time);
    - 6 are "curled" into less than 10^{-33} cm, and thus inferable only by indirect means

Mr. & Mrs. Flat

Why *Now*?

We believe that we are being plunged into a period of time about which the Bible says more than about any other period of time in history,

...including the time that Jesus walked the shores of Galilee and climbed the mountains of Judea.

- Are there "Hidden Messages" in the Bible?

It is the glory of God to conceal a thing:
but it is the honor of kings to search out a matter.

Proverbs 25:2

The Torah Always Points to YHWH

Genesis	Exodus	Leviticus	Numbers	Deuteronomy
תורה →	תורה →	יהוה	← הרות	← הרות
TORH	TORH	**YHWH**	HROT	HROT

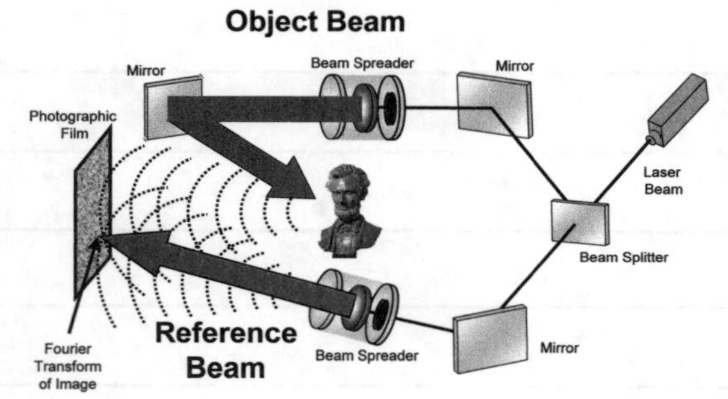

Old Testament Incomplete

- Old Testament:
  - Unexplained ceremonies (sacrificial rituals)
  - Unachieved purposes (the covenants)
  - Unappeased longings (poetical books)
  - Unfulfilled prophecies

Search the scriptures; for in them ye think ye have eternal life: and they are they which testify of me.
John 5:39

Learn the Bible in 24 Hours: Session 1

Hour 1: Introduction

1) How many books are there that make up the "Bible"? How many different writers are represented? Over how many years was it compiled?

2) How can one *prove* that the Bible is of "extraterrestrial" origin?

3) What do you conclude if you encounter a triangle with a sum of more than 180° in the three corners?

4) In how many dimensions to we exist? (Justify your answer.) How many are listed in the Epistle to the Ephesians?

5) How do we know that *time* is a *physical* dimension? Name three physical characteristics with which time varies. How does this impact our understanding of the Biblical text?

Group Discussion Questions: See *Small Group Leaders* section of this workbook.

Preparation for the Next Session:

Read the first three chapters of Genesis.

Learn the Bible

in 24 Hours

Hour 2

The Creation &

The Fall of Man

Genesis 1 - 3

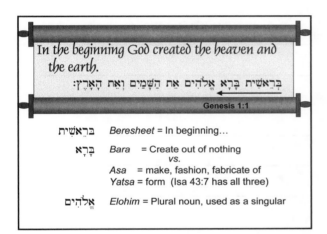

In the beginning God created the heaven and the earth.

בְּרֵאשִׁית בָּרָא אֱלֹהִים אֵת הַשָּׁמַיִם וְאֵת הָאָרֶץ׃

Genesis 1:1

בְּרֵאשִׁית	*Beresheet* = In beginning…
בָּרָא	*Bara* = Create out of nothing *vs.* *Asa* = make, fashion, fabricate of *Yatsa* = form (Isa 43:7 has all three)
אֱלֹהִים	*Elohim* = Plural noun, used as a singular

The "Big Bang" Models

(*"First there was Nothing; then it exploded!"*)

- Steady State Model
  - Einstein's Biggest Mistake
- Hesitation Model
  - Refuted in the 1960's
- Oscillation Model
  - Refuted by entropy laws, lack of mass.
- Inflation Model
  - Requires antigravity forces never observed

Two Imputed Concepts

(Elusive in Our Physical World)

1. Randomness — Prov 16:33
   - Stochastic vs. Deterministic Processes
   - Pseudo-Random Numbers
   - "Chaos Theory"
2. Infinity — Jas 1:17
   - Macrocosm: Finite Universe
   - Microcosm: Quantum Physics

Planck length: 10^{-33} cm.
Planck time: 10^{-43} sec.

∴ *Digital* Simulation

- "Reality" is only Virtual

Young Earth Indicators

- Moon Dust
- Oil Gushers
- Earth's Magnetic Field
- Mississippi River Delta
- Salinity of Oceans
- Poynting-Robertson Effect
- Radiohalos

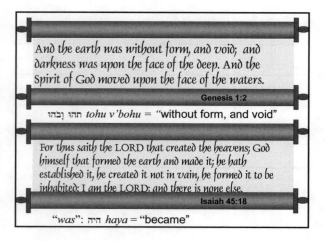

And the earth was without form, and void; and darkness was upon the face of the deep. And the Spirit of God moved upon the face of the waters.

Genesis 1:2

תֹהוּ וָבֹהוּ *tohu v'bohu* = "without form, and void"

For thus saith the LORD that created the heavens; God himself that formed the earth and made it; he hath established it, he created it not in vain, he formed it to be inhabited: I am the LORD; and there is none else.

Isaiah 45:18

"*was*": היה *haya* = "became"

A Missing Interval?

In the beginning God created the heaven and the earth.
***But** the earth **became** without form, and void;*
and darkness was upon the face of the deep.
And the Spirit of God hovered over the face of the waters. Genesis 1:1-2

(Adversative, *"But"*: LXX & Vulgate)

- Originally suggested by Thomas Chalmers, 1814
- Supported by G. H. Pember, D. G. Barnhouse, G. Campbell Morgan, A. Custance, et al;
- Highly speculative but tends to tie with other passages

Setterfield-Norman Analysis

- 1677, Roemer, Io eclipse:
  - 307,600 +/- 5400 km/sec
- 1875, Harvard, (same method):
  - 299,921 +/- 13 km/sec
- 1983, National Bureau of Standards, laser:
  - 299,792.4586 +/- 0.00003 km/sec

Entropy Profile of the Universe

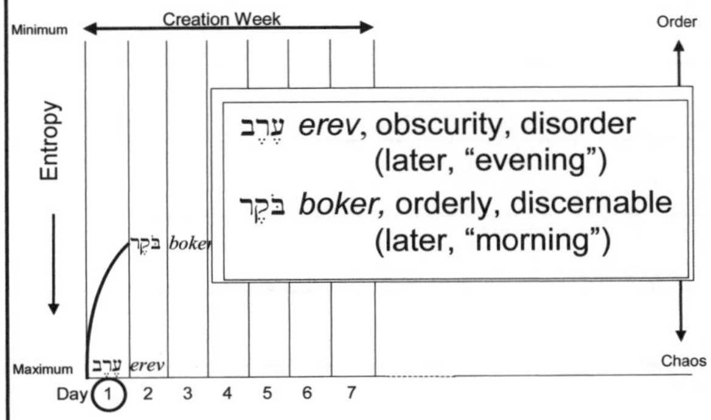

Space is *not* an empty vacuum

"torn": Isaiah 64:1
"worn out" like a garment: Psalm 102:25
"shaken": Hebrews 12:26, Haggai 2:6, Isaiah 13:13
"burnt up": 2 Peter 3:12
"split apart" like a scroll: Revelation 6:14
"rolled up" like a mantle: Hebrews 1:12
or a scroll: Isaiah 34:4

"Zero-Point" Energy

- If the temperature of an empty container is lowered to absolute zero, there still remains a residual amount of thermal energy that can not by any means be removed: the "zero-point energy."
  - A "vacuum" is now known to be a vast reservoir of seething energy out of which particles are being formed and annihilated constantly.

Why doesn't the electron in an atom simply radiate its energy away and spiral into the nucleus?

It picks up energy from the background zero-point energy and therefore is sustained by it.

Death of Darwinism

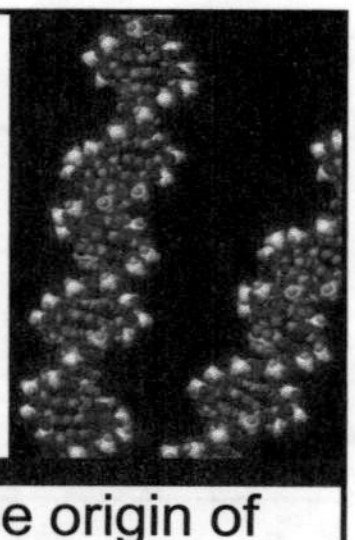

- Advances in Microbiology DNA, et al, have dealt the death blow to Darwinism.
  - DNA is a *digital* code
- Darwinism cannot explain the origin of life because it cannot explain the origin of *information.*
  - Irreducible complexity refutes chance as a designer.

Thermodynamics

1st Law:
Conservation of Matter, Energy
(There's no way to win.)

2nd Law :
Entropy: "The Bondage of Decay"
(You can't even break even.)

Entropy in Scripture

They shall perish… grow old as a garment... *Psalm 102:25-26*

The earth will grow old like a garment... *Isaiah 51:6*

Heaven and earth will pass away... *Matthew 24:35*

Conservation of Matter/Energy

- *And on the seventh day God ended His work…* *Genesis 2:2-3*
- *The works were finished from the foundation of the world…* *Hebrews 4:3-4*
- *All the things that are therein…you preserve them all.* *Nehemiah 9:6*

Genesis 3

The Seed Plot of the Entire Bible

- *Nachash*, the "Shining One"
- The Forbidden Fruit
- Methodology of the Deception
  - Doubt: *"Yea, Hath God Said…?"*
  - then Denial: *"Ye shall not surely die."*
- God's Declaration of War
  - Seed of the Woman
  - Seed of the Serpent

Genesis 3:14-16

And the LORD God said unto the serpent, Because thou hast done this, thou art cursed above all cattle, and above every beast of the field; upon thy belly shalt thou go, and dust shalt thou eat all the days of thy life:

And I will put enmity between thee and the woman, and between ***thy seed and her seed****; it shall bruise thy head, and thou shalt bruise his heel.*

Unto the woman he said, I will greatly multiply thy sorrow and thy conception; in sorrow thou shalt bring forth children; and thy desire shall be to thy husband, and he shall rule over thee…

The Plan of Redemption

The First Act of "Religion":

And the eyes of them both were opened, and they knew that they were naked; and they sewed fig leaves together, and made themselves aprons [covering, armor]. Genesis 3:7

God's Plan of Redemption:

Unto Adam also and to his wife did the LORD God make coats of skins, and clothed them. Genesis 3:21

Teaching them that only by the shedding of innocent blood they would be covered…

(…on another tree in another garden)

Learn the Bible in 24 Hours: Session 2

Hour 2: The Fall of Man (Genesis 1-3)

1) List 12 major doctrines introduced in Genesis.

2) List the key events in each "Day" of Creation.

3) How do the Hebrew verbs *Bara, Asa and Yatsa* differ?

4) Explain how *erev* came to mean "evening." Explain how *boker* came to mean "morning." Why is there no *erev* or *boker* on the 7th Day?

5) List the first two laws of thermodynamics and explain why they are Biblically relevant.

6) What is "entropy" and where is it referred to in Scripture?

7) What led to God's "declaration of war" and against whom was it declared?

8) Who is the "Seed of the Woman"? Who is the "Seed of the Serpent"?

9) What is the first act of "religion" found in the Bible? What was God's instructive response?

Group Discussion Questions: See *Small Group Leaders* section of this workbook.

Preparation for the Next Session:

Read Chapters 4 – 11 of Genesis.

8. [illegible]

9. [illegible] was God's [illegible]?

Group Discussion Questions: See [illegible] section of this workbook.

Preparation for the Next Session:

- Read [illegible]

Learn the Bible
in 24 Hours
Hour Three

The Pre-Historical Period

Genesis 4 - 11

Genesis

Genesis 1, 2	Creation	
Genesis 3	Fall of Man	
Genesis 4	Cain & Abel	Hour 3
Genesis 5	Genealogy of Noah	Hour 3
Genesis 6-9	Flood of Noah	Hour 3
Genesis 10-11	Tower of Babel	Hour 3
Genesis 12-20	Abraham	
Genesis 21-26	Isaac	
Genesis 27-36	Jacob	
Genesis 37-50	Joseph	

Genesis 4

- Cain and Abel
- Offerings
  - Cain's = Fruit of his own labors
  - Abel's = A Lamb
- Cain's offering *rejected*
  - Why?
- Cain murders Abel

A Riddle

- Who is the oldest man in the Bible?
  Methuselah; he lived 969 years.
- Yet he died before his father!
  How can that be?
- His father was Enoch…
  At age 65, something happened;
  he then "walked with God" 300 years…

Genealogy of Genesis 5

Adam	*Man (is)*
Seth	*Appointed*
Enosh	*Mortal*
Kenan	*Sorrow; (but)*
Mahalalel	*The Blessed God*
Jared	*Shall come down*
Enoch	*Teaching*
Methuselah	*His death shall bring*
Lamech	*The Despairing*
Noah	*Comfort, Rest*

One Integrated Design

The New Testament
is in the Old Testament concealed;
The Old Testament
is in the New Testament revealed.

And it came to pass, when men began to multiply on the face of the earth, and daughters were born unto them, that the Sons of God saw the daughters of men that they were fair; and they took them wives of all which they chose.

Genesis 6:1,2

בְּנֵי־הָאֱלֹהִים *Bene HaElohim*

"Sons of God"

בְּנֵי־הָאֱלֹהִים *Bene HaElohim*
= angels

- Old Testament: Job 1:6, 2:1, 38:7
- New Testament: Luke 20:36
- *Book of Enoch*
- *Septuagint* (LXX)

"Daughters of Men"

בְּנוֹת הָאָדָם *benoth adam*

= "daughters of Adam"

(Same as in the earlier part of the same sentence of Genesis 6:1, 2)

The Nephilim

נְפִילִים *Nephilim:* "the fallen ones"

נפל *Nephal*: "to fall, be cast down to fall away, desert"

Septuagint (Greek):

γίγαντες *gigantes* = "giants"?

γίγας *gigas* = "earth-born"

These are the generations of Noah: Noah was a just man and perfect in his generations, and Noah walked with God.

Genesis 6:9

תָּמִים *tamiym* = "without blemish, sound, healthful, without spot, unimpaired"

"Lines of Seth" View

- "Sons of God" ~ Sethite Leadership?
- "Daughters of Adam" ~ Daughters of Cain?
- Sin = failure to maintain separation?
- (Nephilim = ?)

Noah's Ark

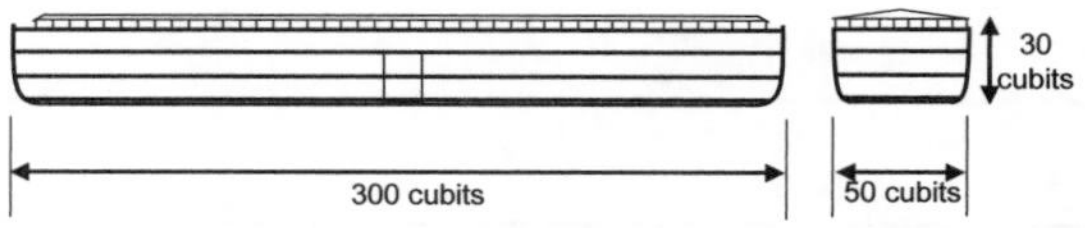

Cubit =	18 inches	450 ft	75 ft	45 ft
	25 inches	625 ft	104 ft	63 ft

Displacement: 65,000 tons?

4.1 million cu/ ft. 340,000 sheep

1400 railroad cars 18,000 species

Geological Mysteries

- Grand Canyon origin
- Mid-Oceanic Mountain ranges
- Submarine Canyons
- Magnetic variations on ocean floor
- Coal and oil formations
- Frozen mammoths
- Metamorphic Rock
- Fossil graveyards
- Jigsaw fit of Continents

The Flood

- Rained 40 days
- Not just rain: "fountains of the deep"
- Waters prevailed 150 days
- In the Ark 377 days
  - 5 months floating
  - 7½ months on the mountain

Some Perspectives

- Only 1 Ark
  - Only 1 door
- No births nor deaths
  - All in the ark were saved
- Alternative Theological Speculations ended when the door was shut. Only 3 groups of people:
  - Those that *perished in* the Flood
  - Those that were *preserved through* the Flood
  - Those that were *removed prior to* the Flood

Noah

Shem (26)	Ham (30)	Japheth (14) = 70
Elam	Cush	Gomer
Asshur	Mizraim	Magog
Arphaxad	Put	Madai
Lud	Canaan	Javan
Aram		Tubal
		Meshech
		Tiras

The Tower of Bab-El

Genesis 11

- One Language: Hebrew
- Godless Confederacy: 1st World Dictator
  - Nimrod – ("We will rebel")
- Plain of Shinar: Bab-El "Tower to Heaven"
  - Astrological Temple
  - Zodiac corrupted
- Tale of Two Cities
  - Babylon – the City of Man
  - Jerusalem – the City of God

Learn the Bible in 24 Hours: Session 3

Hour 3: The Pre-Historical Period (Genesis 4-11)

1) Make a list of the major topics covered in the first 11 chapters of Genesis (and the chapters involved).

2) Where did Cain get his wife?

3) Why was Abel's sacrifice accepted and Cain's rejected?

4) What are the key personal lessons of Genesis 4?

5) Who is the oldest man in the Bible? How could he have died *before* his father?

6) What is the message hidden behind the genealogy in Genesis 5?

7) What is concealed in the Old Testament? How? What is revealed in the New Testament? How?

8) Who were the *"Sons of God"* in Genesis 6? How do we know? Who were the *Nephilim*? Why is this important to understand?

9) How big was Noah's Ark? (length, width, height, and volume). (How many railroad car equivalents?)

10) How many of each animal were on the ark? How long were they on the ark?

11) Where did "civilization" begin? Who was the first world dictator?

Group Discussion Questions: See *Small Group Leaders* section of this workbook.

Preparation for the Next Session:

Read Genesis 12 – 50.

Learn the Bible
in 24 Hours

Hour Four

The Patriarchs

Genesis 12 - 50

Genesis

Genesis 1, 2	Creation	
Genesis 3	Fall of Man	
Genesis 4	Cain & Abel	
Genesis 5	Genealogy of Noah	
Genesis 6-9	Flood of Noah	
Genesis 10-11	Tower of Babel	
Genesis 12-20	Abraham	Hour 4
Genesis 21-26	Isaac	Hour 4
Genesis 27-36	Jacob	Hour 4
Genesis 37-50	Joseph	Hour 4

Terah's Family

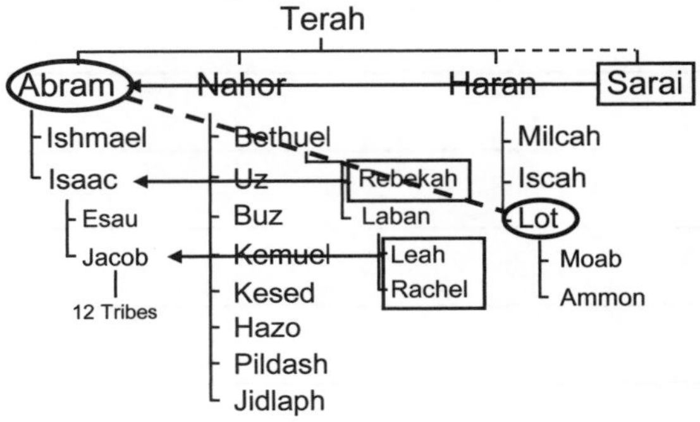

7 "I Wills"

1. And I will make of thee a great nation,
2. and I will bless thee,
3. and make thy name great;
4. and thou shalt be a blessing:
5. And I will bless them that bless thee,
6. and curse him that curseth thee:
7. and *in thee shall all families of the earth be blessed.*

Genesis 12:2-3

Three Major Promises

- God's Covenant with Abraham
  - In his seed all nations shall be blessed
- God's Covenant with the Nation Israel
  - If they faithfully served Him they'd prosper
  - If they forsook Him they would be destroyed
- God's Covenant with David
  - His family would produce the Messiah who would reign over God's people forever

Unconditional Covenant

Genesis 15

A divinely ordered ritual:

barath,"To cut a covenant"
(Participants would divide a sacrifice, and together, in a figure "8," would repeat the terms of the covenant)

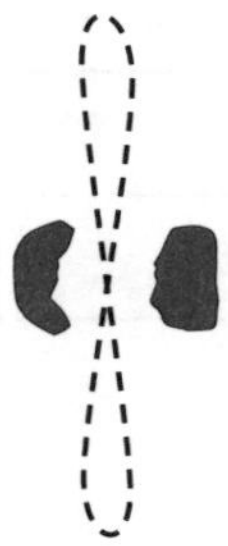

Here God goes it alone;
It is *unconditional*.

Abrahamic Covenant

- Commitment of the Land to his descendants
  - "from the river of Egypt to the great river, the River Euphrates"
- Afflicted in Egypt: 400 years Acts 7:6
  - (in Egypt 430 years) Ex 12:40
- But will return with great possession

The Terms of the Covenant

- Declared eternal and unconditional
- Re-confirmed by an oath: Gen 22:15-18
- Confirmed to Isaac and to Jacob: Gen 26:2-5 *(despite their acts of disobedience);*
- NT declares it immutable: Heb 6:13-18

Abram ⟶ Abraham

Genesis 17

- Changed his Name to Abraham
- Confirmed His Covenant: "Father of Many Nations"
- Instituted Circumcision as a sign
- Also changed *Sarai* to *Sarah*
- Promised him a son

Sodom & Gomorrah

Genesis 19

- Two angels visit Lot
- The homosexuals seek the visitors
  - Lot offers his virgin daughters instead
  - The angels blind the attackers
- Lot's family evacuated
  - As a *prerequisite* condition to judgment
- *Jesus likened His return to these days!*

Luke 17:29

And Isaac spake unto Abraham his father, and said, My father: and he said, Here am *I, my son. And he said, Behold the fire and the wood: but where* is *the lamb for a burnt offering?*

And Abraham said, My son, God will provide himself a lamb for a burnt offering: so they went both of them together.

Genesis 22:7,8

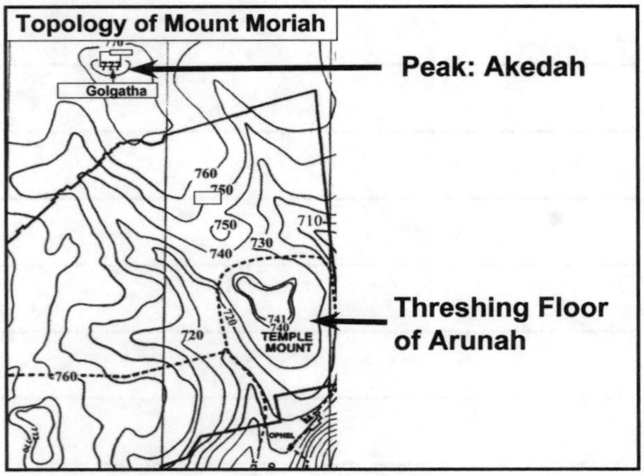

And the LORD said unto her, Two nations are in thy womb, and two manner of people shall be separated from thy bowels; and the one people shall be stronger than the other people; and the elder shall serve the younger.

Genesis 25:23

- Esau: the firstborn
- Jacob:
  - Purchases the Birthright from Esau
  - Obtains Jacob's blessing thru deceit

Wrestling to the End of Self

Gen 29: Jacob cheated by Laban
Gen 30: 12 Tribes born
Gen 31: Jacob returns to the Land
Gen 32: Jacob wrestles; renamed Israel
Gen 33: Jacob reconciled to Esau
Gen 34: Sin the family; Dinah revenged
Gen 35: Jacob returns to Bethel; Benjamin born; Rachel dies

The Career of Joseph

Genesis 37-50

- Joseph, favored: Firstborn of Rachel,
  - Coat "of many colors"
  - Dreams of ascendancy
    - Sheaves
    - Sun, Moon, Stars
- Sold into slavery by his brothers
- Imprisoned by Potiphar
- Interprets dreams
  - Butler
  - Baker

The Ascendancy of Joseph

- Pharaoh's Dreams
  - 7 Fat Cows, 7 Lean Cows
  - 7 Plump Heads of Grain, 7 Thin Heads
- Joseph called to interpret
- Joseph appointed Prime Minister of Egypt
- Famine brings his brothers to beg for food
  - Keeps Simeon as a hostage for Benjamin
  - 2nd Visit: Benjamin with them
- Jacob and the family migrate to Egypt

> *The sceptre shall not depart from Judah, nor a lawgiver from between his feet, until Shiloh come; and unto him shall the gathering of the people be.*
>
> **Genesis 49:10**

Sceptre: their tribal identity and the right to apply and enforce Mosaic Laws

Shiloh: to whom it belongs; the Messiah

The Descendants of Abraham

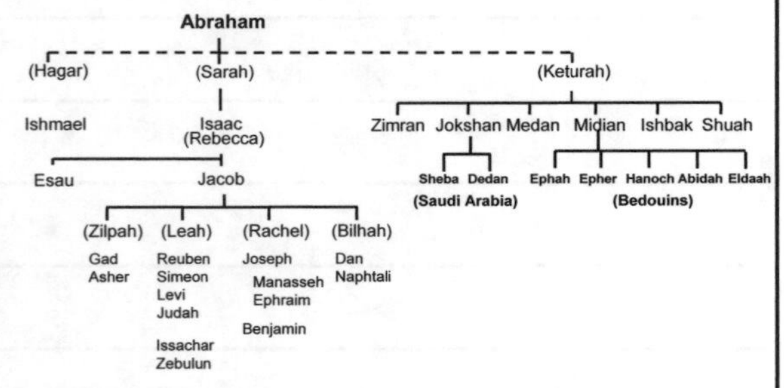

Learn the Bible in 24 Hours: Session 4

Hour 4: The Patriarchs (Genesis 12-50)

1) List and summarize the chapters that deal primarily with Abraham; Isaac; Jacob; and, Joseph.

2) List the seven "I wills" of Genesis 12:2-3.

3) Summarize the three major promises God made with: Abraham; the nation Israel; and David.

4) What is the significance of the *unconditional* nature of the covenant in Genesis15? How do we know that it was unconditional?

5) In what several ways did Jacob defraud his brother Esau? In what ways did Isaac deceive Jacob? In what ways was Jacob deceived regarding Joseph?

6) In what ways was the career of Joseph *prophetic* of Jesus Christ?

Group Discussion Questions: See *Small Group Leaders* section of this workbook.

Preparation for the Next Session:

Familiarize yourself with the remainder of the Torah: Exodus, Leviticus, Numbers, and Deuteronomy.

Learn the Bible
in 24 Hours
Hour Five

The Birth of the Nation

Exodus, Leviticus, Numbers, Deuteronomy

The Torah

Genesis	The Book of Beginnings	
Exodus	The Birth of the Nation	Hour Five
Leviticus	The Law of the Nation	Hour Five
Numbers	The Wilderness Wanderings	Hour Five
Deuteronomy	The Laws Reviewed	Hour Five

Three Major Promises

- God's Covenant with Abraham
  - In his seed all nations shall be blessed
- God's Covenant with the Nation Israel
  - If they faithfully served Him they'd prosper
  - If they forsook Him they would be destroyed
- God's Covenant with David
  - His family would produce the Messiah who would reign over God's people forever

The Book of Exodus

(The "Outgoing")

- Entire race shedding the shackles of generations-long servitude
- Migrating to a new country, emerging in a new *corporate* life
- They entered Egypt as a family; They emerged from Egypt as a nation.
- *Is there any more amazing national spectacle in all of history?*

Ten Plagues

"…against all the gods of Egypt I will execute judgment…"

Exodus 12:12

• Water turned to blood	Osiris, Isis, Horus, Hapimon,Tauret, Nu
• Frogs	Hekt
• Lice (Sand Flies?)	Geb
• Scarabs ("Swarms")	Amon-Ra
• Murrain in animals	Apis, Hathor, Bubastis
• Boils (Ashes)	Thoth, Apis, Serapis, Imhotep
• Hail, Fire	Shu, Nut, Horus
• Locusts	Nepri, Ermutet, Anupis, Osiris
• Darkness (that was felt)	Ra, Aten, Horus, Tem, Shu
• Firstborn	Pharaoh's own dynasty

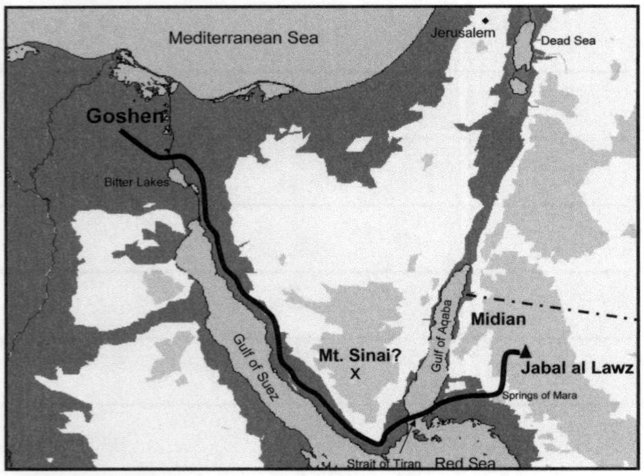

The Ten Commandments

- Thou shalt have no other gods before me.
- Thou shalt not worship any graven image.
- Thou shalt not take the name of the Lord thy God in vain.
- Remember the Sabbath Day to keep it holy.

- Honor thy father and thy mother.
- Thou shalt not murder.
- Thou shalt not commit adultery.
- Thou shalt not steal.
- Thou shalt not bear false witness.
- Thou shalt not covet.

Why Was the Law Given?

Romans 7

1. Law was given to expose our sin nature; 7:7
2. To incite the sin nature to sin more! 7:8-23

   Sin nature cannot been reformed
3. To drive us to despair of self-effort 7:24, 25
4. To drive us to dependence upon the Holy Spirit alone 8:1-4

The Tabernacle

"The House of Blood"

- In addition to the famed Two Tablets of the Law, Moses also received a set of engineering specifications for a portable sanctuary.
- The Scriptures devote more space to the description of the Tabernacle than any other single subject.

"The Word was made flesh and *tabernacled* among us..."
John 1:14

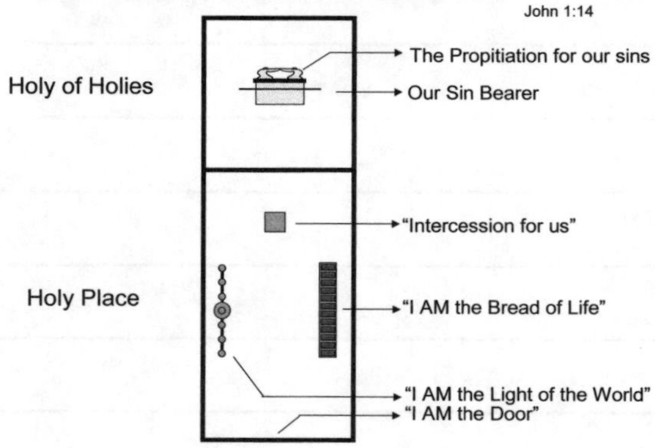

Leviticus

(to be studied rather than just read)

- Requirements for Fellowship: Holiness
  - Precepts of His Law: Standards, Conduct
  - Penalties attaching to violations
- Ground for Fellowship: Sacrifice
  - Anticipatory of *the ultimate* Sacrifice
- The Walk of Fellowship: Separation
  - Preparation for the Coming Messiah

"Appointed Times"

Leviticus 23

52	sabbaths
+ 7	days of Passover (including its related feast days)
+ 1	*Shavout,* Feast of Weeks (Pentecost)
+ 1	*Yom Teruah,* Feast of Trumpets
+ 1	*Yom Kippur,* Day of Atonement
+ 7	days of *Sukkot,* Feast of Tabernacles
+ 1	*Shimini Atzeret,* 8th Day of Assembly
70	

The Feasts of Israel

The Spring Feasts (1st Month: Nisan)
- Passover
- Feast of Unleavened Bread
- Feast of First Fruits

Feast of Weeks

The Fall Feasts (7th Month: Tishri)
- Feast of Trumpets
- Yom Kippur
- Feast of Tabernacles

Numbers

- Hebrew: *Be-midbar*, "In the Wilderness"
  - (Greek: *Arithmoi;* Latin: *Numeri*)
    - Includes 2 census takings of the nation
- Resumes where Exodus left off
- It is a book about arrested progress:
  - It took only 40 hours to get Israel out of Egypt
  - It took 40 years to get Egypt out of Israel

The Camp of Israel

Numbers 2

Judah	74,600	**Ephraim**	40,500
Issachar	54,400	Manasseh	32,200
Zebullun	57,400	Benjamin	35,400
	186,400		**108,100**
Reuben	46,500	**Dan**	62,700
Simeon	59,300	Asher	41,500
Gad	45,650	Naphtali	53,400
	151,450		**157,600**

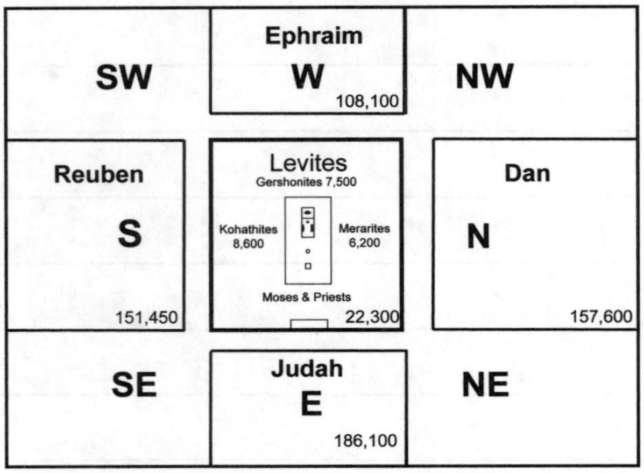

Deuteronomy

- The bridge between the first 4 (outside the Land) and the next 7 (inside the Land).
- *Sh'ma*: The Great Commandment
- More quotes by Jesus than from any other book.
- Song of Moses
- The Death of Moses
  - Michael fights with Satan over the body
  - Transfiguration appearance
  - One of the two witnesses in Revelation 11?

> Hear, O Israel: The LORD our God is one LORD: And thou shalt love the LORD thy God with all thine heart, and with all thy soul, and with all thy might.
>
> **Deuteronomy 6:4,5**

"One" = אֶחָד *echad*: compound unity; collective sense plurality in unity; ("one cluster of grapes")
vs. *yacheed*, absolute unity (never of YHWH)
(יְהוָה YHWH, ("*LORD*"), appears 3 times)

Learn the Bible in 24 Hours: Session 5

Hour 5: The Birth of the Nation (Exodus - Deuteronomy)

1) List the five books of the *Torah* and the key concept in each.

2) List the Ten Plagues and the characteristics of each.

3) List the Ten Commandments and contrast them with the Sermon on the Mount in Matthew 5-7.

4) Why was the Law given? (List four reasons: Romans 7 & 8.)

5) Make a floor plan view of the Tabernacle showing the seven elements of "furniture." Identify each with a claim of Christ.

6) List the seven Feasts of Israel and their commemorative roles.

6) Make a sketch of the Camp of Israel (in relative scale and with Scriptural annotations).

7) Which book in the Old Testament is most often quoted from by Jesus Christ?

Group Discussion Questions: See *Small Group Leaders* section of this workbook.

Preparation for the Next Session:

Read Joshua, Judges, and Ruth.

[illegible] Scriptural foundation)

[illegible]

Group Discussion Questions [illegible]

Preparation for the Next Session

Read Joshua 1 [illegible]

Learn the Bible
in 24 Hours
Hour Six

In The Land

Joshua, Judges, Ruth

The Book of Joshua

- Entering the Land 1 – 5
  - Crossing the Jordan
  - Circumcision at Gilgal
    - Manna ceases…
  - The Night Visitor
- Overcoming the Land 6 - 12
- Occupying the Land 13 - 24
  - The victory of faith.

The Conquest of Canaan

- The Conquest of Jericho
- The Failure at Ai
- The Battle at Beth-Horon
- The Division of the Land

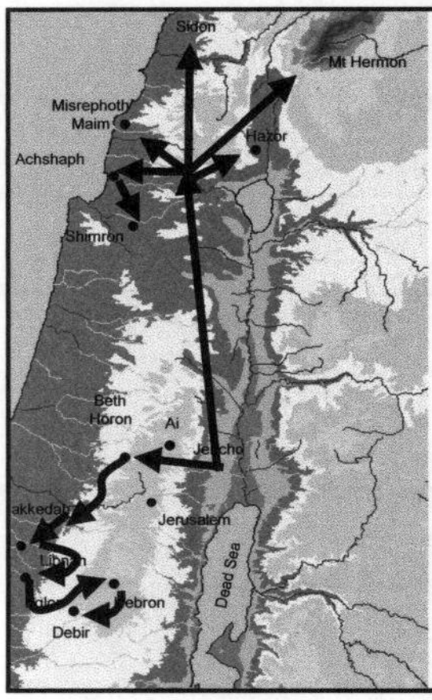

The Campaign

North Joshua 11

King Jabin of Hazor's alliance

Slower guerilla war..

South Joshua 10

Treaty with Gibeonites

Battle of Beth Horon

Quick surprise attacks

Joshua vs. Ephesians

Victorious Christian Living

Joshua	**Ephesians**
Israel	Church
Entering & Possessing	Entering & Possessing
Earthly Inheritance	Heavenly Inheritance
Given in Abraham	Given in Christ

- Each opened by a Divinely Appointed Leader
- Each given by Grace; received by Faith
- Each the sphere of striking divine revelations
- Each a scene of warfare and conflict

Joshua vs. Revelation

- (*Yehoshua* is a variant of *Yeshua*)
- A military commander dispossessing the usurpers
- 7-year campaign
  - Against 7 (of an original 10) nations
- Torah ignored at Jericho: (Sabbath ignored; Levites involved)
  - First sent in "Two Witnesses"
  - Seven Trumpet Events
  - (preceded by "Silence in heaven for ½ hour")
- Enemies confederated under a leader in Jerusalem
  - *Adoni-Zedek, "Lord of Righteousness"*
- Ultimately defeated with
  - Hailstones and fire from heaven
  - Signs in the Sun, Moon, etc.
- Kings hide in caves; ("Rocks fall on us…")

Division of the Land

The Tribes were allocated their portions by casting lots.

Levites were assigned to 48 cities, six of which were designated "Cities of Refuge"

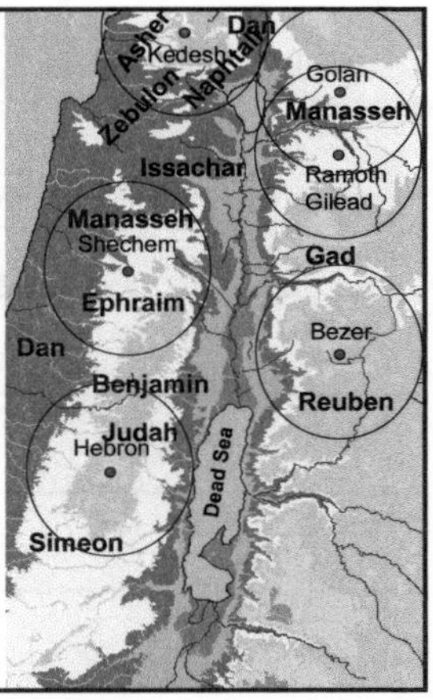

Cities of Refuge

- Available in cases of manslaughter
  - Not premeditated murder

    Was the Crucifixion of Christ premeditated or manslaughter?
- Secured against the Avenger of Blood
  - As long as abiding in the City of Refuge

    How secure are we in Christ?
- Prevailed until the High Priest died

  Who is our High Priest? When did He die?

Daughters of Zelophehad

- Torah exception on rules of inheritance
  - Requested of Moses — Numbers 27:1-11
  - Granted by Joshua — Joshua 17:3-6
- Husband *adopted* by father of the bride

  Ezra 2:61=Neh 7:63; Num 32:41, cf. 1 Chr 2:21-23, 34-35
- (Anticipates the lineage of Christ…)

Judges

- ~450 years following the Conquest
- 400-year segments of Nation's history:
  - Birth of Abram to death of Joseph ~400 yrs
  - Death of Joseph to Exodus ~400 yrs
  - Exodus to the Monarchy period ~400 yrs
  - The Monarchy period to the Exile ~400 yrs
- A record of occasional deliverers rather than a succession of governors, probably written by Samuel prior to the accession of David.
- "Everyone did what was right in their own eyes."

The Lessons

- Six servitudes
  - Not accidents
  - Brought on by YHWH as punishments
  - Privileges are not license to *sin*
- The Pattern:
  - Sinning
  - Suffering
  - Repentance
  - Deliverance

The Book of Ruth

- Love's Resolve Chapter 1
  -Ruth cleaving to Naomi
- Love's Response Chapter 2
  - Ruth gleaning
- Love's Request Chapter 3
  - The Threshing Floor Scene
- Love's Reward Chapter 4
  - The Redemption of both Land and Bride

Ruth Gleaning

Chapter 2

- The Law of Gleaning Lev 19:9,10; Deut 24:19-2
  - Provision for the Destitute
- "Happens" upon the field of Boaz
  - Boaz = "In Him is Strength" (Temple Pillar)
  - Introduced by "Unnamed Servant"
  - Protection + "Handfuls on purpose…"
- *Goel*: Kinsman-Redeemer
  - Law of Redemption Lev 25:47-50
  - Law of Levirite Marriage Deut 25:5-10

The Threshing Floor

Chapter 3

- Naomi recognizes an opportunity
  - For the redemption of her land
  - For a new life for Ruth
  - She instructs Ruth on what to do
- Ruth approaches Boaz
  - To fulfill the role of a *Goel*
- A "nearer kinsman" in the way . . .
- (6 measures of barley = a code for Naomi)

The Redemption

Chapter 4

- Boaz confronts the "Nearer Kinsman"
  - He is willing to redeem the property;
  - He is not willing to take Ruth as bride
  - He yields his shoe to relieve the obligation
- Boaz steps up
  - He purchases the land for Naomi
  - He "purchases" Ruth as bride
  - "May your house be like Perez…"

Typological Analysis

- *Goel* = Kinsman-Redeemer
  - Must be a Kinsman
  - Must be Able to perform
  - Must be Willing
  - Must assume all the obligations
- Boaz = The Lord of the Harvest
  The Kinsman-Redeemer
- Naomi = Israel
- Ruth = Gentile Bride

Observations

- In order to bring Ruth to Naomi, Naomi had to be exiled from her land.
- What the Law could not do, Grace did.
- Ruth does not replace Naomi.
- Ruth learns of Boaz's ways thru Naomi
- Naomi meets Boaz thru Ruth
- No matter how much Boaz loved Ruth, he had to wait for *her* move.
- Boaz, not Ruth, confronts the Nearer Kinsman.

Ruth: Final Remarks

- Book of Ruth always read at the Feast of Pentecost (*Shavout*).
- You can't really understand Revelation 5 without understanding the Book of Ruth.
- *You and I are also beneficiaries of a love story, that was written in blood, on a wooden cross, erected in Judea almost 2,000 years ago.*

Learn the Bible in 24 Hours: Session 6

Hour 6: In the Land (Joshua, Judges, Ruth)

1) The key battles in the conquest of Canaan included: a) Jericho and b) Beth Horon. Summarize the *prophetic* lessons of each.

2) What are the *personal* lessons from the defeat at Ai?

3) Which tribe did not get a land allocation? What did they inherit instead?

4) In what ways did the Cities of Refuge precursor Jesus Christ?

5) Sketch a (rough) map of the allocations of the land to the Tribes following the conquest.

6) In what way does the claims of Christ depend upon the exceptions granted the daughters of Zelophehad?

7) Sketch a time line of four 400-year segments of Israel's history.

8) What is the repetitive pattern of failures in the period of the Judges?

9) What four requirements did a *Goel*, or Kinsman-Redeemer, fulfill?

10) In what ways is the Book of Ruth a book of *prophecy*? List at least seven. Compare it with Revelation 5.

Group Discussion Questions: See *Small Group Leaders* section of this workbook.

Preparation for the Next Session:

Familiarize yourself with the historical books of Samuel, Kings and Chronicles (2 volumes each).

Learn the Bible
in 24 Hours
Hour Seven
The Monarchy:
Samuel, Kings, Chronicles

© Koinonia House, Inc.

The Rise & Fall of the Monarchy

- 1st & 2nd Samuel (LXX: 1st & 2nd "Kingdoms") (Latin Vulgate: "Kings")
  - Samuel
  - Saul
  - David
- 1st & 2nd Kings (LXX: 3rd & 4th "Kingdoms") (Latin Vulgate: "Kings")
  - David's 40 year reign
  - Solomon
  - The Divided Kingdom
  - The Exile: Assyria and Babylon
- 1st & 2nd Chronicles
  - Recap of the **Southern Kingdom: Judah**

The 1st Book of Samuel

- Samuel – The Last of the Judges 1 - 7
  - Birth and youth
  - Call and Office
  - Times and Acts
- Saul – The First of the Kings 8 –15
  - Appointment as king
  - Promising Beginning
  - Later Folly and Sin
- David – The Greatest of the Kings 15 – 31
  - Anointing by Samuel
  - Service before Saul
  - Years as a fugitive

The 2nd Book of Samuel

- David's Triumphs 1 – 12
  - King of Judah (at Hebron) 7 yrs
  - King of All Israel (at Jerusalem) 13 yrs
- David's Troubles 13 - 24
  - In his Family
  - In the Nation

The Davidic Covenant

2 Samuel 7

- *Affects all that follows*
  - in the Scriptures
  - in the history of mankind
- Divine Confirmation of throne in Israel
- Perpetuity of the Davidic Dynasty
- Davidic Covenant is Unconditional
- Messianic Implications

Key Points

- Divine Confirmation of throne in Israel
- Perpetuity of the Davidic Dynasty
- Davidic Covenant is Unconditional
- Messianic Implications

  "Son of David, Son of Abraham" Matt 1:1

  "Lion of the Tribe of Judah, Root of David" Rev 5:5

David's Turning Point

- His Great Sin
  - (Honesty of the Scriptures)
  - Adultery; then murder
- Culmination of a *Process*
  - Prosperous ease
  - Self-indulgence
    - Accumulating wives forbidden — Deut 17:17
- Remorse and Repentance — Psalm 51
  - *"A man after God's own heart…"* — 1 Sam 13:14, Acts 13:22

The 1st Book of Kings

"Discontinuance through Disobedience"

- King Solomon — 40 years — 1-11
  - Accession
  - Temple Built
  - Zenith of Fame and Glory
  - Declension and Decease
- Divided Kingdom — 80 years — 12-22
  - Accession of Rehoboam
  - Kings of Southern Kingdom ("Judah")
  - Kings of Northern Kingdom ("Israel")
    - The Prophet Elijah

Solomon

- Personally
  - Brilliant, but lacked moral vigor
  - Excessively Self-indulgent
- Historically
  - Peak of Israel's prosperity
  - Visit of the Queen of Sheba
  - "Solomon in all his glory…"
- Typically
  - Positive: Millennial Reign?
  - Hidden Negative? (Salary = 666; et al)

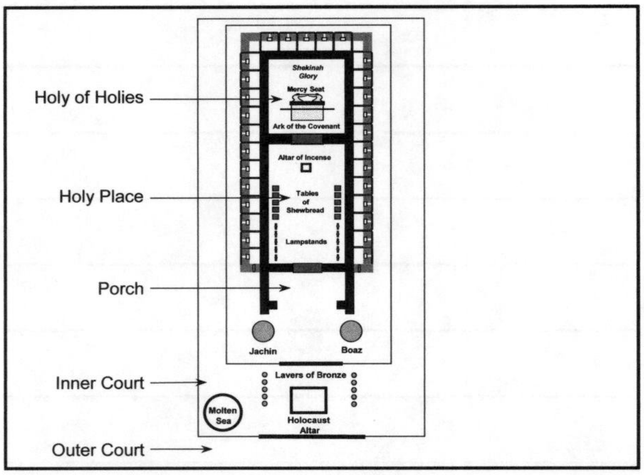

Our Personal Architecture?

- 7 Times declared:
  "Ye are the Temple of God"
  - 1 Cor.3:9-17; 6:19; 2 Cor. 6:16; Eph. 2:20,21; Heb. 3:6; 1 Pet. 2:5; 4:17.
- Appears to hold the key to our "software" architecture:
  - Heart?
  - Soul?
  - Spirit?
  - Mind?

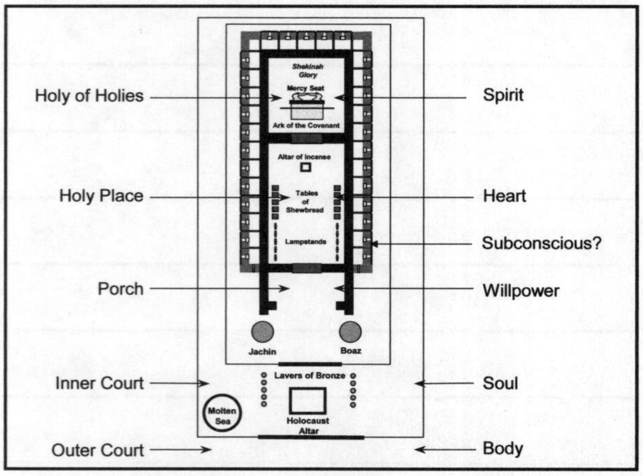

The 2nd Book of Kings

(The most tragic national record ever written)

- Annals of Israel, the Northern Kingdom 1-10
  - Ministry of Elisha
  - To the death of Jehu, Israel's 10th king
- Alternating Annals of *Both* Kingdoms 11-17
  - (Jonah, Amos, and Hosea prophesy)
  - To the Assyrian Captivity of Israel
- Annals of Judah, The Southern Kingdom 18-25
  - (Obadiah, Joel, Isaiah, Micah, Nahum, Habakkuk, Zephaniah, and Jeremiah prophesy)
  - Ends with the Babylonian Captivity of Judah

The Two Kingdoms

- The Northern Kingdom – Israel
  - 19 Kings reigned 250 years
  - 7 different dynasties
  - Assyrian Captivity, 721 BC (no return)
- The Southern Kingdom – Judah
  - 20 Kings reigned 370 years
  - 1 dynasty: The Davidic
  - Babylonian Captivity, 606 BC (70 years)

Judah
The Southern Kingdom

975 BC ↑	Rehoboam	17
	Abijam	3
	Asa	**41**
	Jehoshaphat	**25**
1st Kings		
2nd Kings		
	Jehoram	8
	Ahaziah	1
	Athaliah	6
	Joash	40
	Amaziah	29
	Azariah (Uzziah)	**52**
370 yrs		
	Jotham	**16**
	Ahaz	16
	Hezekiah	**29**
	Manasseh	55
	Amon	2
	Josiah	**31**
	Jehoahaz	(3 mos)
	Jehoiakim	11
	Jehoiakin	(3 mos)
↓	Zedekiah	11
606 BC	**Babylonian Captivity**	

Israel
The Northern Kingdom

975 BC ↑	Jeroboam	Bad	22
	Nadab	↓	2
	Baasha		24
	Elah		2
	Zimri		(1 wk)
	Omri		12
	Ahab		22
1st Kings	Ahaziah		2
2nd Kings	Jehoram		12
	Jehu		28
	Jehoahaz		17
	Jehoash		16
	Jeroboam II		41
	Interregnum		12
250 yrs	Zechariah		½
	Shallum		(1 mo)
	Menahem		10
	Pekahiah		2
	Pekah		20
↓	Hoshea	**Worse**	9
721 BC	**Assyrian Captivity**		

The 1st Book of Chronicles

The House of YHWH

- Israel's Main Genealogies 1 - 9
  - Adam to Jacob
  - Jacob to David
  - David to Zedekiah
  - Tribal Allotments
- David's Reign at Jerusalem 10 - 29
  - Anointed of the Lord
  - The Ark of the Lord
  - The Covenant of the Lord
  - The Temple of the Lord

The 2nd Book of Chronicles

The Temple vs. The Throne

- Solomon's 40 Years' Reign 1 – 9
  - Early Establishment
  - Building the Temple
  - All His Glory
- Judah's History to the Exile 10 – 36
  - The Division of the Kingdom
  - The 20 Kings of Judah
  - Deportation to Babylon

The Monarchy

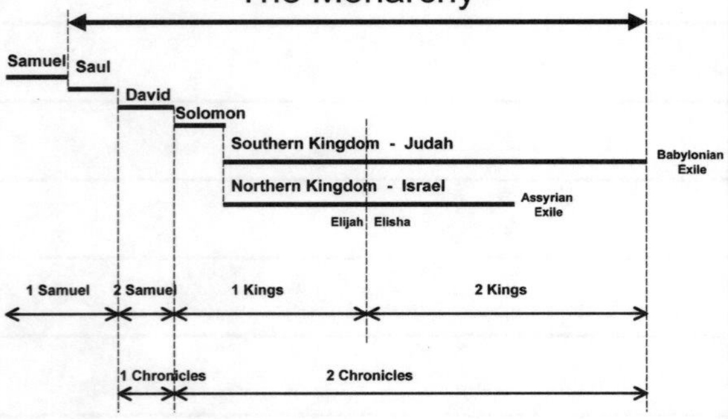

Learn the Bible in 24 Hours: Session 7

Hour 7: The Monarchy (Samuel, Kings, Chronicles)

1) Sketch a time profile of the Monarchy, including the major leadership from Samuel to the Babylonian Exile, showing how the six books overlap their coverage.

2) In what ways was David "a man after God's own heart"? What were his major failures?

3) What were the main features of the Davidic Covenant? What are the Messianic implications?

4) How did Solomon's Temple differ from the Tabernacle? Sketch the two, with the *spiritual* architecture similarities.

5) Contrast the histories of the Northern and Southern Kingdoms.

Group Discussion Questions: See *Small Group Leaders* section of this workbook.

Preparation for the Next Session:

As time permits, familiarize yourself with the Book of Job, Psalms, Proverbs, Ecclesiastes, and Song of Songs.

Learn the Bible

in 24 Hours

Hour Eight

The Poetical Books

The Book of Job

A Dramatic Poem framed in an Epic Story

- The Prologue 1, 2
  - Satan's Challenge
- The Dialogues 3 - 37
  - Eliphaz, the Temanite
  - Bildad, the Shuhite
  - Zophar, the Naamathite
  - Elihu, the Buzite
- The Divine Response 37 - 42
  - Science Quiz
  - Epilogue

Insights

- Satan is accountable to God
- Satan's dark mind is an open book to God
- Satan is behind the evils that curse the earth
- Satan is neither omnipresent nor omniscient
- Satan can do nothing without Divine permission
- God's eyes are ever on His own

Scientific Insights

- Hydrological cycle
  - Evaporation, circulation, precipitation Job 28:24-27
  - How do clouds stay aloft?
  - Air, wind, have weight
  - Water weighs more than air; how supported?
- Space/Time/Mass universe
  - "He stretcheth out the north over empty space, and hangeth the earth upon nothing" Job 26:7
  - The "morning stars singing" at the foundation of the earth? Job 38:7

Astronomical Insights

- "Where is the way where light dwelleth?"
  - Light is dynamic; darkness is static Job 38:19
- "Canst thou bind the influences of the Pleiades, or loose the bands of Orion?"
  - These are the only visible eye constellations in direct gravitational bondage Job 38:31
- *Mazzeroth* (Zodiac) are signs of God's plan of redemption Job 38:12

Psalms

Israel's Hymnal

- Poetry laced with strong theology
- Hebrew, *Tehillim*: "Praises"
  - 55 addressed to "the chief musician"
- Greek:
  - *psalmoi*, "a poem to be sung to a stringed instrument"
  - *psaltar*, for harp or stringed instrument

Selah

It is commonly assumed that this refers to musical instructions; however:

- *selah* is to connect subject matter, not music
- It connects the end of one strophe with the beginning of the next; it is the connecting of the two subjects together
- Sometimes synthetic; sometimes antithetic
- Concerned with truth, not tunes

Special Terms

• *Aiieleth-Shahar*	The hind of the morning; dawn
• *Alamot*	The maidens' choir
• *Al-Tashchith*	Destroy not
• *Gittith*	Winepresses (Autumn)
• *Jeduthun*	Praise-giver (1 of 3 directors of worship)
• *Jonath-Elem-Rechokim*	Dove of distant woods (of David in flight)
• *Mahalath*	The Great Dancing
• *Maschi*	Instruction; understanding
• *Michtam*	Engraven (emphasized; permanent)
• *Muth-labbeyn*	Death of the Champion
• *Negionoth*	Stringed Instruments
• *Nehiloth*	Inheritances
• *Sheminith*	8th group or division
• *Shiggaion*	A crying aloud (grief or joy)
• *Shoshannim*	Lilies (Springtime)

Messianic Details

2, 8, 16, 22, 23, 24, 40, 41, 45, 68, 69, 87, 89, 102, 110, 118, et al

- His Person
  - Son of God — 2:7; 45:6,7; 102:25,27
  - Son of Man — 8:4-6; etc
  - Son of David — 139:3,4,27,29
- His Offices
  - Prophet — 22:22, 25; 40:9,10
  - Priest — 110:4
  - King — 2; 24; 72; etc

The Shepherd Psalms

- The Suffering Savior **Psalm 22**
  - The Good Shepherd John 10
- The Living Shepherd **Psalm 23**
  - The Great Shepherd Hebrews 13
- The Exalted Sovereign **Psalm 24**
  - The Chief Shepherd 1 Peter 5:4

Other Psalm Groups

- Hallelujah Psalms 106, 111, 112, 113, 135, 146-150
- Penitential Psalms 6, 32,38, 39, 51,102,143
- Imprecatory Psalms 35, 57, 59, 69, 83, 109, 137, et al
- Acrostic Psalms 9, 25, 34, 37, 111, 112, 119, 145

Psalm 119:

22 sections (for each Hebrew letter)

Each section of 16 lines in 8 couplets,

Each couplet beginning with same letter of the Hebrew alphabet

The Book of Proverbs

- Prudence through Precept
  - Proverbs is to our practical life what Psalms is to our devotional life.
- *Pro:* for; *verba*: words, terse maxim
- A proverb does not argue; it assumes.
- Solomon wrote 3,000 1 Kings 4:32
- Arranged during the reign of Hezekiah

Organization of Proverbs

1) Extolling of Wisdom 1-9
   - 15 Sonnets (rather than Proverbs)
   - 2 monologues
2) Maxims Enjoining Prudence 10-24
   - 375 aphorisms in couplets
   - 16 epigrams
3) More Maxims on Prudence 25-31
   - 7 epigrams
   - 55 couplets
   - 13 sayings of Agur
   - Oracle of Lemuel's mother
   - Acrostic on the Virtuous Woman

Colorful Imagery

- Contrastive:
  "A fair woman without discretion is like a jewel of gold in a swine's snout"
- Completive:
  "As cold water to a thirsty soul is like good news from a far country"
- Comparative:
  "The tongue of a nagging woman is a continual dripping in a very rainy day"

Ecclesiastes

- Hebrew: *Koheleth*, the Preacher
- Solomon's sermon on the *natural man's* quest for the chief good
- A cumulative treatise of component parts
- Concludes: "All is Vanity"
- Bravely honest rather than pessimistic
- Sees beyond life's ironies and wearing repetitions to Divine control and future restitutions

The Book of Ecclesiastes

- The Quest by Personal Experiment 1 – 2
  - Search for wisdom and pleasure
- The Quest by General Observation 3 – 5
  - Ills and enigmas of human society
- The Quest by Practical Morality 6 - 8
  - Material things cannot satisfy the soul
- The Quest Reviewed and Concluded 9 - 12
  - Vanity of Vanities: All is vanity

Song of Songs

- Theme: (Ultimate) Love
- No book of Scripture has given rise to more commentaries and opinions
  - Allegorical?
  - Literal?
- Key: Psalm 45, A Song of Loves
  - A royal marriage hymn
  - The Heavenly Bridegroom

The Story Behind the Opera

- Solomon is the hero of the piece
  - *Shulamit* is the Cinderella of the piece
- Handsome stranger promises to return
  - Family skeptical during extended absence
- The King has sent for you
  - It's the handsome shepherd!
- "I am my beloved's, and his desire is toward me."

Learn the Bible in 24 Hours: Session 8

Hour 8: The Poetical Books

1) What does the reader of the Book of Job know that Job doesn't? What do we learn about Satan in the first few chapters?

2) List the "friends" of Job. What makes Elihu different?

3) Compile some of the issues that emerge in God's "science quiz" in Chapters 37-39.

4) Who wrote the Psalms?

5) Diagram the three speakers in Psalm 2.

6) In what way does it appear that Psalm 22 was written "first person singular" while hanging on the cross?

7) Who wrote most of the Proverbs?

8) Summarize the opera of the Song of Songs.

Group Discussion Questions: See *Small Group Leaders* section of this workbook.

Preparation for the Next Session:

Read the Book of Daniel.

Learn the Bible

in 24 Hours

Hour Nine

Daniel

The Book of Daniel

Hour 9

- Historical 1 - 6
  - Nebuchadnezzar's Dream 2
  - His Fiery Furnace 3
  - His Ego Trip 4
  - The Fall of Babylon 5
  - The Revolt of the Magi 6
- Prophecies 7 - 12
  - The Times of Gentiles 2, 7, 8
  - The Seventy Weeks 9
  - The Dark Side 10
  - The Final Consummation 11,12

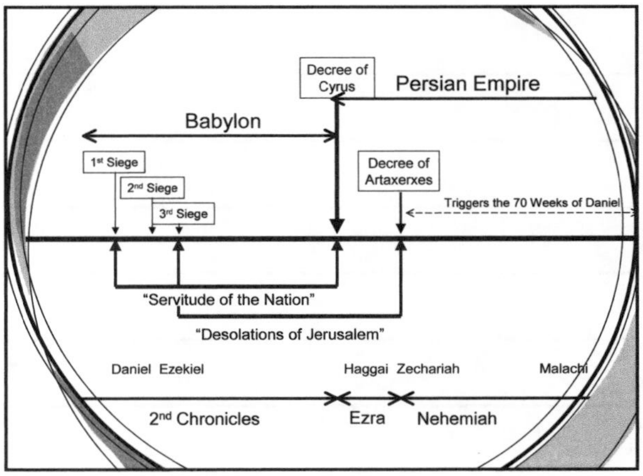

Nebuchadnezzar's Dream
Daniel 2

Gold		**Babylon**
Silver		**Persia**
Brass		**Greece**
Iron		**Rome I**
Iron + Clay		**"Rome II"**

The Times of the Gentiles

- Daniel 2 thru Daniel 7:
  Aramaic, not Hebrew
- Daniel's prophecies are a rare glimpse of *Gentile* history, in advance!
- The "Times of the Gentiles"
  - began with Nebuchadnezzar
  - will end when the Coming World Leader is displaced by the Return of the Lion of the Tribe of Judah, The Root of David…

Bow or Burn!
Daniel 3

- Ego trip: All gold image, 60 x 6 cubits
- Follow the music…
- Daniel's 3 friends refuse!
- Furnace x 7! (Guards destroyed)
- Only their bindings burned…
  - A Fourth as a visitor!?
- Typological conjectures…
  Where was Daniel?

Nebuchadnezzar's Testimony

Daniel 4

- Nebuchadnezzar's 2nd Dream
  - Great Tree, hewn down for 7 years
- Daniel interprets…
- 1 Year later,
  - Nebuchadnezzar stricken with mental derangement for 7 years
  - (Daniel was his personal nurse)
- Nebuchadnezzar recovers and publishes the entire testimony throughout the world

The Fall of Babylon

Daniel 5

- Belshazzar (Nebuchadnezzar's grandson) throws a party for 1,000 nobles
- The Persian army is on their near horizon
- The fingers of a hand are seen writing on the wall of the banquet hall…
- Daniel is called to interpret
- Unknown to them, that night the Persian Army was able to slip through and conquer Babylon without a battle…

The Handwriting on the Wall

יטת יטת אדכ וגח
מנא מנא תקל פרס

$\mathbf{M^{e}n^{e}}$: Numbered, Reckoned.
"God hath numbered thy kingdom and finished it."
Your number is up.

$\mathbf{T^{e}k^{e}l}$: Weighed.
"Thou art weighed in the balances, and art found wanting."

$\mathbf{P^{e}r^{e}s}$: Broken, Divided.
"Thy kingdom is divided, and given to the Medes and the Persians."

($\mathbf{P^{a}r^{a}s}$ is also the word for Persians.)

The Book of Daniel

The Prophecies

Chapter 7 The Four Beasts
Chapter 8 The Ram and the Goat
Chapter 9 The Seventy Weeks
Chapter 10 The Dark Princes
Chapter 11 The Gentile Successions
Chapter 12 The Consummation of All Things

Daniel's Visions Compared

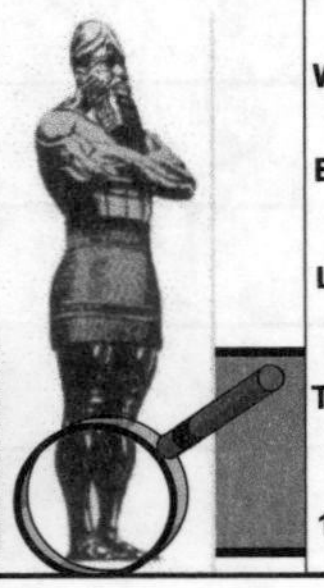

Daniel 2	Daniel 7	
Gold	Winged Lion	Babylon
Silver	Bear on side	Persia
Brass	Leopard	Greece
Iron	Terrible Beast	Rome I
Iron + Clay	10 Heads...	"Rome II"

The Roman Empire, Phase I

68 BC Rome emerges
44 BC Julius Caesar assassinated
31 BC Battle of Actium
64 AD Nero begins his persecutions
284 AD Diocletian divides it into 2 (legs?)
312 AD Constantine moves to Byzantium
476 AD Empire breaks into pieces

Each remaining segment has had its era . . .

The "70 Weeks" of Daniel

The Scope	9:24
The 69 Weeks	9:25
(The Interval)	9:26
The 70th Week	9:27

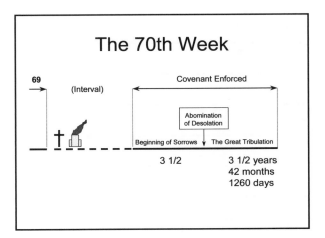

The 69 Weeks

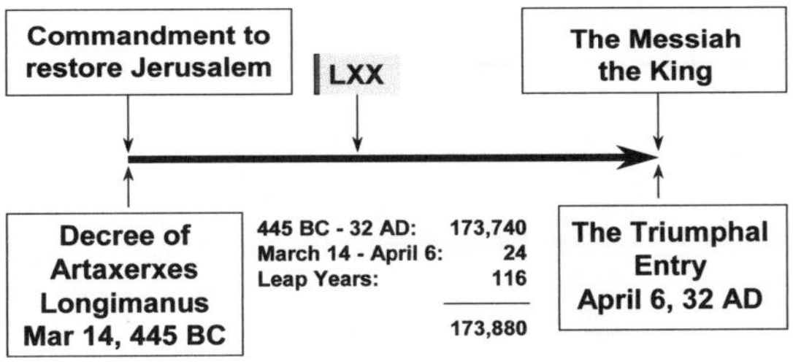

The 70th Week

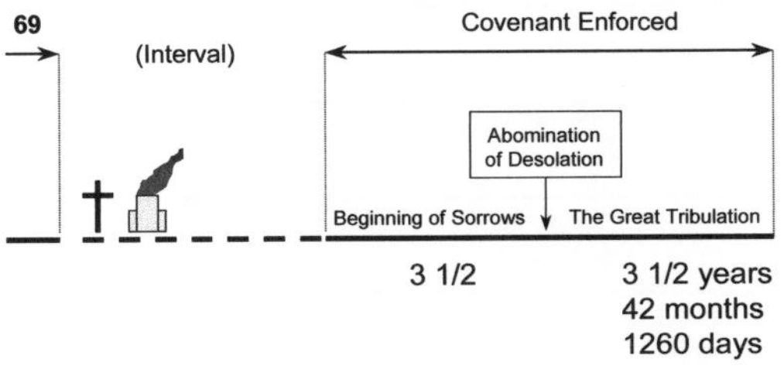

Daniel 10

A Glimpse of the Dark Side

- Daniel fasts for 21 days
- An Angel is sent,
  - but is withstood for 21 days by "The Prince of the Kingdom of Persia"
  - until assisted by "Michael, the Chief Prince"
- After giving Daniel the subsequent vision (Chapters 11 & 12) he will have to deal with "The Prince of the Power of Greece"

Daniel 11 & 12

- A detailed profile of the subsequent kings or the Seleucid and Ptolemaic Dynasties confronting one another.
- Includes a detailed glimpse of the final World Ruler that will prevail until the end times.

  (More on this will be dealt with separately later in this series.)

The Ultimate Issue

- We are in possession of a message of extraterrestrial origin.
- It portrays us as objects of an unseen warfare.
- Our eternal destiny depends upon our relationship with the ultimate victor in this cosmic conflict.
- Where do *you* stand with respect to *Him*?

Learn the Bible in 24 Hours: Session 9

Hour 9: The Book of Daniel

1) How do we know that the Book of Daniel is authentic?

2) How is the Book of Daniel organized? List the chapters in *chronological* order. Which chapters are written in Aramaic? Why?

3) What are the *prophetic* implications suggested by the fiery furnace of Chapter 3?

4) Diagram the dream of Nebuchadnezzar and Daniel's interpretation. Compare it with the four visions of Chapter 7.

5) Which chapter was written—and published—by a Gentile king? Why?

6) Are there secret messages in the Bible? Explain the "handwriting on the wall" of Daniel 5.

7) Detail the last four verses of Daniel 9: a) How do we know they involve "weeks" of *years*? b) What is the *scope* of Gabriel's prophecy? c) To whom is the prophecy directed? d) How did the "69 weeks" get fulfilled? e) How do we know that there is an *interval* between the 69th and 70th "week" of years? f) What is the "Abomination of Desolation"? g) What event concludes the "70th week"

8) Where do you find the 400 "silent years" in your Bible?

Group Discussion Questions: See *Small Group Leaders* section of this workbook.

Preparation for the Next Session:

Read the post-exile books of Ezra, Nehemiah, and Esther.

Learn the Bible
in 24 Hours
Hour Ten

Post-Exile History

Ezra, Nehemiah, Esther

Hour 10
The Post-Exile Period

- The Decree of Cyrus
  - Isaiah's Letter
- Ezra
  - The Mixed Multitudes
- Nehemiah
  - The Decree for Jerusalem
- Esther
  - The Drama
  - [Acrostics]
- Inter-testament Period

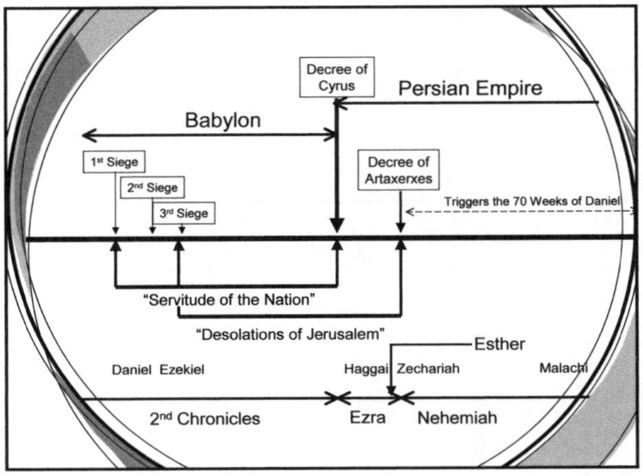

Cyrus II ("The Great")

- Established the Medo-Persian Empire
  - Cyrus' father: Cambyses I (600-559 BC), was king of Anshan (E. Elam)
  - Cyrus' mother: Mandane, a daughter of Astyages, king of Media
- 550 BC: Attacked his father-in-law, the corrupt Astyages;
  - Captured Ecbatana without a battle
- Welded the Medes and Persians into a unified nation that continued for two centuries

The Conquest of Babylon

- October 12, 539 BC, Cyrus' general captured Babylon without a battle.
- The Persians diverted the River Euphrates into a canal upriver so that the water level dropped "to the height of the middle of a man's thigh," which thus rendered the flood defenses useless and enabled the invaders to march through the riverbed to enter by night. Herodotus

The Letter to Cyrus

- When Cyrus made his grand entrance Daniel presented him with an ancient scroll of Isaiah, which contained a personal letter *addressing him by name.*

  Josephus, *Antiquities,* XI, I, 2
- *Isaiah had died 150 years before Cyrus was born!*

Cyrus' Response

- Cyrus was duly impressed.
- He freed the captives and even gave them incentives to return to their homeland and rebuild their temple.

Ezra

- Probable author of 1 & 2 Chronicles also
  - 1 & 2 Chronicles, Ezra, Nehemiah = 1 book
- Credited with establishing the "canon"
- Return of the Remnant
  - 536 BC: 49,697 under Zerubbabel
  - 456 BC: (80 years later) under Ezra

Kings of Persia

• Cyrus the Great (Mede/Persian)	Ezra 1, Isaiah 45
• Cambyses	Ahasuerus of Ezra 4
• Gaumata	Artaxerxes of Ezra 4
• Darius I "Hystaspis"	Ezra 5, 6
• **Xerxes I**	Ahasuerus of Esther
• **Artaxerxes I ("Longimanus")**	Nehemiah 2
• Xerxes II	
• Darius II "Nothus"	Nehemiah 12
• Artaxerxes II "Mnemon"	
• Artaxerxes III "Ochus"	
• Darius III "Codomanus"	Nehemiah 12

The Drama

- Lavish Royal Banquet
  - Queen Vashti refuses to immodestly display herself
  - Forfeits her royal diadem
- Esther, orphaned Jewish girl, raised by her cousin Mordecai, selected as replacement
- Mordecai thwarts a plot against the king

The Deadly Threat

- Haman succeeds in getting the king to order the extermination of all the Jews
- Mordecai prevails upon Esther to intercede
  - "Thou art come for such a time as this"
  - "If I perish, I perish."
- She asks for 3 days of fasting and prayer

The Critical Moment

- Esther enters the inner court
  - The king extends his scepter
- She invites the king and Haman to a banquet
- She demurs: she invites them to a subsequent banquet…

What a day brings…

- A gloating Haman prepares a gallows
- A sleepless king reads the chronicles
  - Mordecai was never rewarded for his deed
- Haman unknowingly specifies Mordecai's reward

The 2nd Banquet

- Esther asks for her life to be spared
- An astonished king ponders Haman's deceits
- Haman falls on Esther's couch to plead
- The king, returning, misconstrues the move and orders Haman hanged…
  - …on the very "gallows" he built for Mordecai

The Denoument

- Haman's estate escheat to the crown
  - Set under Mordecai's supervision
- A second decree authorizes the Jews to defend themselves
  - 127 provinces, from India to Ethiopia
  - Magistrates also assist them…
- Celebrated as The Feast of Purim

The Book of Esther

- Name of God does not appear?
- Esther = "Something Hidden"
- Hidden Codes:

  5 Acrostics

  3 Equidistant Letter Sequences

The Greek Empire

- Alexander conquers the Persians 332 BC
- Succeeded by his 4 generals:
  - Cassander — Macedonia & Greece
  - Lysimacus — Thrace, Bithynia, most of Asia Minor
  - Ptolemy — Egypt, Cyrene, Arabia

    Sponsored the Septuagint Translation: LXX 270 BC
  - Seleucus — Syria and East to India

    Antiochus Epiphanes (The "Little Horn") Dan 8

The Roman Empire, Phase I

63 BC	Pompey conquers Judea Herod Antipater, an Edomite, appointed ruler
40 BC	Parthians conquer Judea
37 BC	Romans regain Judea Herod the Great succeeds Antipater
31 BC	Battle of Actium
~2 BC?	Registration and Census ordered
7 AD	Caponius appointed Procurator Removed legal powers of Sanhedrin

"Woe unto us for the scepter has departed from Judah and the Messiah has not come!" Babylonian Talmud

Learn the Bible in 24 Hours: Session 10

Hour 10: Post-Exile History (Ezra, Nehemiah, Esther)

1) Sketch a time line of the Babylonian Captivity, marking the "servitude of the Nation" and the "desolations of Jerusalem," the relevant imperial decrees, and the respective coverage of the historical books and the prophets' ministries.

2) Where do you find a personal letter written to Cyrus the Great *150 years before he was born*? What was its effect on the history of Israel?

3) Which book deals with the frustrations of attempting to rebuild the *Temple* unprotected? Summarize.

4) Which book deals with the authority to rebuild the *city* of Jerusalem? Summarize.

5) Which book deals with a "Hitler-like" plot to destroy all the Jews? Summarize the principal personae and the resulting drama.

Group Discussion Questions: See *Small Group Leaders* section of this workbook.

Preparation for the Next Session:

Read the major prophets: Isaiah, Jeremiah, & Ezekiel. (Daniel we covered separately.)

Learn the Bible
in 24 Hours
Hour Eleven

The Major Prophets

The Prophet Isaiah
The Messianic Prophet

- Quoted in the NT more than any other prophet
- Style loftier than Shakespeare, Milton, or Homer
- One of the greatest discoveries of the Dead Sea Scrolls was a complete copy of the Book of Isaiah.

Overview

Principal Messages

- Judgment for lack of loyalty, sin
- Coming Restoration (Nevertheless)
- Coming Messiah through House of David

Stylistic Peculiarities

- Telescoping Perspectives
  - Dynamic "focal lengths": near & distant
  - Double References
- Incidental insights en route

Highlights

- Messianic Prophecies
  - (exceeded only by Psalms)
- Vision of the Throne of God 6
- The Incarnation 7, 9
- The Doom of Babylon 13, 14
- The Fall of Lucifer 14
- Letter to Cyrus 45
- The Messiah and His Atonement 53
- The Second Coming 63
- The Millennium 65, 66
- Addendum: Two Isaiahs?

Isaiah 53

3 He is despised and rejected of men; a man of sorrows, and acquainted with grief: and we hid as it were *our* faces from him; he was despised, and we esteemed him not.

4 Surely he hath borne our griefs, and carried our sorrows: yet we did esteem him stricken, smitten of God, and afflicted.

5 But he *was* wounded for our transgressions, *he was* bruised for our iniquities: the chastisement of our peace *was* upon him; and with his stripes we are healed.

6 All we like sheep have gone astray; we have turned every one to his own way; and the LORD hath laid on him the iniquity of us all.

12 Key Points

- Comes in absolute lowliness: "a root out of a dry ground"
- He was "Despised and rejected of men"
- Suffered for sins, and in the place of, others: ourselves!
- God Himself caused the suffering to be vicarious
- Absolute resignation: "He opened not his mouth."
- Died as a felon, "from prison and judgment"
- Cut off prematurely, "out of the land of the living"
- Personally guiltless; "no violence nor deceit in his mouth"
- He was to live on after his sufferings: "prolong his days"
- YHWH's "pleasure would prosper in his hand"
- Mighty triumph after his suffering: "Divide spoil…"
- By all this God "would justify many"

Ministry Mandate

The Spirit of the Lord GOD is upon me;
because the LORD hath anointed me
to preach good tidings unto the meek;
He hath sent me to bind up the brokenhearted,
to proclaim liberty to the captives, and the opening of the prison to them that are bound;
To proclaim the acceptable year of the LORD, and the Day of Vengeance of our God…

Isaiah 61:1,2

Jeremiah

The Weeping Prophet

- Commissioned 1
- Prophecies Before the Fall of Jerusalem
  - General and Undated 2 - 20
  - Specific and Dated (Last 4 of Judah's kings) 21 - 39
- Prophecies After Fall of Jerusalem 40 - 44
  - Carried to Egypt
- Prophecies Upon Gentile Nations
  - Egypt, Philistines, Moab, Ammon, Edom, Damascus, Elam 45 - 59
  - Doom of Babylon 50 - 51
- Jerusalem Overthrown 52

Highlights

- Key Theme
  - The Process of Divine Judgment in National Life
  - God has not abandoned His Throne
  - – Jerusalem: "I will punish; I will restore"
- Specifies precisely the 70 year captivity 25
  - – Blood Curse on Jeconiah
    Thus saith the LORD, Write ye this man childless, a man that shall not prosper in his days: for no man of his seed shall prosper, sitting upon the throne of David, and ruling any more in Judah. 22:30
- The New Covenant 31:31
- The Doom of Babylon 50, 51

The Doom of Babylon

- Destruction of Babylon — Isaiah 13, 14; Jeremiah 50, 51
  - "Never to be inhabited"
  - "Building materials never reused"
  - "Like Sodom and Gomorrah"
- Fall of Babylon — 539 BC
  - Without a battle
  - Became Alexander's capital
  - Atrophied over the centuries
  - Presently being rebuilt
- "Mystery Babylon?" — Revelation 17-18

The Book of Ezekiel

- Present Judgments on Jerusalem
  - Similes and visions
  - 430 "Days"? — 4
- The Future Destinies of the Nations
  - Origin & Destiny of Satan — 28
- Restoration of the Nation Israel
  - The Valley of Dry Bones — 36, 37
  - Gog and Magog — 38, 39
- The Millennium — 40-48

Vision of the Throne of God

Ezekiel 1 & 10 (Cf. Isaiah 6, Revelation 4)

Cherubim	Camps	Gospels
Lion	Judah	Matthew
Ox	Ephraim	Mark
Man	Reuben	Luke
Eagle	Dan	John

The Origin of Satan

- Isaiah 14
  - The 5 "I Wills"
- Ezekiel 28
  - "The Anointed Cherub that Covereth"
- Revelation 12
  - Summary of Satan's attempts to thwart the Plan of Redemption

The Valley of Dry Bones

Ezekiel 37

- A Vision of the Restoration of Israel
  - Brought back to life in the flesh
  - Later, breathed with the Spirit
- *"The Lord shall set his hand again the second time to recover the remnant of his people…"* Isaiah 11:11
- Fulfilled in the 1st half of 20th century

The Millennial Temple

Ezekiel 40 - 48

- Description of Millennial Temple
  - Highly detailed (not simply symbolic?)
  - All nations to worship there
  - Offerings and sacrifices resumed
  - (Open only on the Sabbath Day and New Moons)
- There is an event that occurs *after* the restoration and *before* the Millennium:

The Magog Invasion
Ezekiel 38 & 39

- The occasion in which God Himself intervenes to quell the ill-fated invasion of Israel by Magog and its allies
  - Persia, Cush, Phut, Libya, Gomer, Togarmah, Meshech, Tubal
- The passage appears to anticipate the use of nuclear weapons.

Nuclear Weapons?

- Left-over weapons provide all the energy for the nation Israel for 7 years
- Professionals hired to clear the battlefield
  - They wait 7 months; then clear for 7 months
  - Bury the dead east of the Dead Sea (downwind)
- If a traveler finds something the professionals have missed, he doesn't touch it: he marks the location and lets the professionals deal with it.

The Disturbing Hint?

And I will send a fire on Magog, and among them that dwell carelessly in the isles: and they shall know that I am the LORD.

Ezekiel 39:6

The more you know about the details of the text in Ezekiel 38 and 39, and

The more you know about the current geopolitical horizon,

The more it seems that it this is getting into position to happen soon…

Learn the Bible in 24 Hours: Session 11

Hour 11: The Major Prophets (Isaiah, Jeremiah, Ezekiel)

1) What prophet is quoted in the New Testament more than any other prophet? Which prophet is known as the Messianic prophet? Provide Bible references.

2) List (6-8) major topics covered by Isaiah? Also, list the key points made in Isaiah 53.

3) Who decisively refuted the notion of "two Isaiahs"? How?

4) Why is Jeremiah known as the "weeping prophet"?

5) How are Isaiah's and Jeremiah's prophecies concerning the doom of Babylon relevant to *today's* headlines?

6) Explain how the lion, ox, man and eagle relate to the camps of Israel, the four Gospels, and the cherubim around the throne of God.

7) Compare the descriptions of Satan in Isaiah 14 and Ezekiel 28.

8) How is the Vision of the Dry Bones in Ezekiel 37 relevant to *today*?

9) For what two reasons are Ezekiel 38 and 39 so familiar to prophecy buffs today?

10) Where is the description of the Millennial Temple detailed?

Group Discussion Questions: See *Small Group Leaders* section of this workbook.

Preparation for the Next Session:

Familiarize yourself with the 12 "minor" prophets.

Learn the Bible
in 24 Hours
Hour Twelve
The "Minor" Prophets

The Book of Hosea

- Prologue 1 – 3
  - Gomer
    - Jezreel
    - Lo-ruhamah
    - Lo-Ammi
- National Sin: Intolerable 4 – 7
- National Sin: Shall be punished 8 – 14

Hosea's Message

Although a loving and caring God had provided their abundance and prosperity;

Their sin, disloyalty and abandonment of Him will force Him to vindicate His justice with judgment.

Thus, God is going to *use their enemies* as His instrument of judgment. Shortly they will be history.

IS THERE A PARALLEL WITH AMERICA??

The Book of Joel

- An Alarm: Invasion by Plague 1-2:11
- An Appeal:
  - "Turn ye to me" 2:12-17
  - "I will restore" 2:18-27
- The Day of YHWH 2:28-3:21
  - End of the present age Revelation 6 – 19
  - Unprecedented plagues Matthew 24:21, 22

The Book of Amos

- The Ultimate Rule of David
- Judgment against 8 "burdens": 1 -2
  - Gaza,
  - Tyre
  - Edom
  - Ammon
  - Moab
  - Judah
  - Israel
- Three Sermons 3 - 6
- Five Visions 7 - 9

The Book of Obadiah

- From Southern Kingdom
- Destruction of Edom
- Esau: "Red"; Mt. Seir (S of Dead Sea to G of Aqaba)
  - Bozrah (Petra, Sela) Capital
  - Fierce, cruel, proud, profane
  - Enemy of Israel Num 20:14-22
    - Active alliance with Israel's destroyers
- Sentence: Poetic justice
- Extinction Nabateans (Arab tribe) …

The Book of Jonah

- The Storm 1
  - Why did he flee?
- The Fish 2
  - Did this really happen?
- The City 3
  - Why Nineveh?
- The Lord 4
  - Why Chapter 4?

Ten Miracles

1) The Storm
2) Selection of Jonah as guilty
3) Sudden subsisting of the storm
4) Great fish: (at the right time and place!)
5) Preservation of Jonah
6) Ejection--safe and sound--on dry land
7) The Gourd
8) The Worm(s)
9) East wind
10) **Repentance of entire city of Nineveh!**

Foreshadows Israel's History

- Disobedient to heavenly commission
- Out of their own land
- Precarious refuge among the Gentiles
- Everywhere a source of trouble
- Yet witnessing to the true God
- Cast out by the Gentiles
- Miraculously preserved amid their calamities
- Calling on YHWH at last
  - 3rd day: Cf. Hosea 6:1ff

The Book of Micah

- Imminent Judgment Declared 1 - 3
  - Assyrians will strike at Egypt
  - Will march through Micah's neighborhood on Judah
- Ultimate Blessing Promised 4 - 5
  - Incarnation: Matt 2:5; Mic 5:2
  - Key truth: *Ruler* yet to come…
- Present Repentance Pleaded 6 - 7
  - Last days…

The Book of Nahum

- Nineveh's Doom
  - Declared
  - Described
  - Deserved
- Decisive test of prediction: fulfillment

The Book of Habakkuk

- A Burden: An agony of perplexity
  - The ostensible silence, inactivity, and apparent unconcern of God
  - Why would God use a people far more wicked than Judah themselves?
- A Vision
  - "The Just Shall Live By Faith" 2:4
- A Prayer
  - "Rest in the day of tribulation" 3:16

Habakkuk 2:4

The Just Shall Live By Faith Romans 1:17

The Just Shall Live By Faith Galatians 3:11

The Just Shall Live By Faith Hebrews 10:38

The Book of Zephaniah

- Wrath Coming Upon Judah 1:1 – 2:3
- Wrath Upon All Nations 2:4 – 3:8
  - West, East: Philistia, Moab, Ammon
  - South, North: Ethiopia, Assyria
- After Wrath, Healing 3:9 – 3:10
  - Conversion of Gentile nations
  - Restoration of Covenant People

The Book of Haggai

- Message to Arouse 1:1-15
- Message to Support 2:1-9
- Message to Confirm 2:10-19
- Message to Assure 2:20-23

The Book of Zechariah

- Early Prophecies:
  The Temple being Rebuilt 1-8
- Later Prophecies:
  After Temple Rebuilt 9-14
  - The Second Coming

The Book of Malachi

- Final Message to a Disobedient People
- (May account for segmenting of the initial week of Gabriel's prophecy of the 70 Weeks: the ceasing of prophecy with Malachi.)

The "Silent Years"

Between the Testaments

- Antiochus Epiphanes 167 BC
  - The Abomination of Desolation
- The Maccabean Revolt 165 BC
  - The Hasmoneans
- The Roman Conquest 63 BC
  - Appoint Herod king
- 400 years of silence
  - Until an angel visits Zechariah…

Learn the Bible in 24 Hours: Session 12

Hour 12: The Minor Prophets

1) List the 12 "minor" prophets and their key messages.

2) What *two* prophets came from Galilee? To whom were they sent?

3) What was Hosea's message to the Northern Kingdom?

4) List the 10 miracles in the Book of Jonah. Which one was the greatest?

5) Where was the Messiah to be born? How did Herod find out?

6) What passage in Habakkuk is the key verse in a trilogy of epistles: Romans, Galatians, and Hebrews?

7) Which prophet provides the key to reconciling the literal Babylon of Isaiah and Jeremiah with Revelation 17 & 18?

8) Which prophet provides the key to *all* financial problems? Explain.

9) Where do we find the "silent years" between the testaments *anticipated*?

Group Discussion Questions: See *Small Group Leaders* section of this workbook.

Preparation for the Next Session:

Hour 13 is a bridge between the Old and New Testaments. It explores, "How Sure Can We Be?"

Learn the Bible

in 24 Hours

Hour Thirteen

How Sure Can We Be?

Prophetic Scriptures

- 8,362 predictive verses
- 1,817 predictions
- 737 separate matters

J. Barton Payne, *Encyclopedia of Biblical Prophecy*

The Tenach

- The Old Testament was translated into Greek by 270 BC.
- There are over 300 prophecies detailing the Coming Messiah.
- We are going to examine only 8 of them.

8 Prophecies

Micah 5:2	Bethlehem	1:100,000
Zechariah 9:9	King on Donkey	1:100
Zechariah 11:12	30 pieces of Silver	1:1,000
Zechariah 11:13	Temple, Potter, etc.	1:100,000
Zechariah 13:6	Wounds in hands	1:1,000
Isaiah 53:7	No defense; innocent	1:1,000
Isaiah 53:9	Died with wicked Grave with rich	1:1,000
Psalm 22:16	Crucified	1:10,000
		?

Composite Probabilities

- If a population has 60% male and 40% female, what is the probability that one taken at random is female?

  40%, or p = 0.4

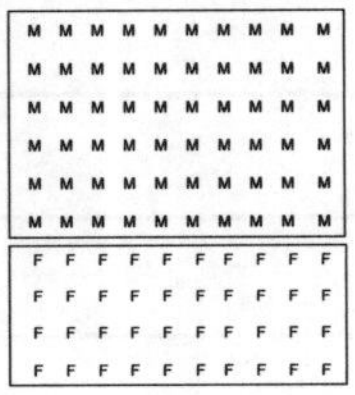

Composite Probabilities

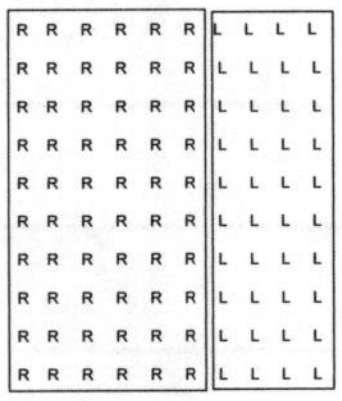

If a population is 60% right-handed and 40% left-handed, what is the probability that someone taken at random is left-handed?

40%, or p = 0.4

Composite Probabilities

What is the probability of selecting a left-handed female?

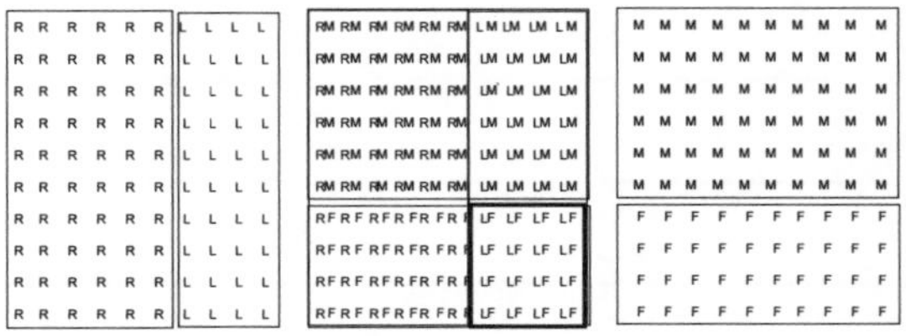

P = 0.4 P = 0.4 x 0.4 = .16 P = 0.4

8 Prophecies

Micah 5:2	Bethlehem	1:100,000
Zechariah 9:9	King on Donkey	1:100
Zechariah 11:12	30 pieces of Silver	1:1,000
Zechariah 11:13	Temple, Potter, etc.	1:100,000
Zechariah 13:6	Wounds in hands	1:1,000
Isaiah 53:7	No defense; innocent	1:1,000
Isaiah 53:9	Died with wicked Grave with rich	1:1,000
Psalm 22:16	Crucified	1:10,000
		1:10^{28}

8 Prophecies Combined

- Total population ≤ 100 billion (10^{11})
- Combined probabilities:

$$10^{28}/10^{11} = 10^{17}$$

The State of Texas, 2 ft. deep

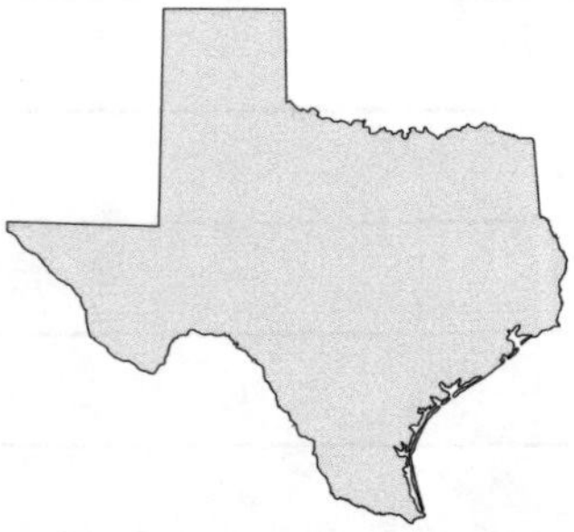

16 Prophecies Combined

- Over 300 to choose from;
- Assuming no *decrease* in likelihoods:
  $10^{28} \times 10^{28} = 10^{56}$
- $10^{56}/10^{11} = 10^{45}$

48 Prophecies Combined

- (Over 300 to choose from)
- Assuming no decrease in likelihoods:

$10^{28} \times 10^{28} \times 10^{28} \times 10^{28} \times 10^{28} \times 10^{28} = 10^{168}$

$10^{168}/10^{11} = 10^{157}$

The Most Amazing Ones

- His detailed genealogy
- Old Testament Messianic Prophecies
- The prediction of the precise day that He would present Himself as King to Jerusalem

The Stratagems of Satan

• Corruption of Adam's line	*Gen 6*
• Abraham's seed	*Gen 12, 20*
• Famine	*Gen 50*
• Destruction of male line	*Exo 1*
• Pharaoh's pursuit	*Exo 14*
• The populating of Canaan	*Gen 12:6*
• Against David's line	*2 Sam 7*

Attacks on David's Line

• Jehoram kills his brothers	*2 Chr. 21*
• Arabians slew all (but Ahazariah)	
• Athaliah kills all (but Joash)	*2 Chr. 22*
• Hezekiah assaulted, etc.	*Isa 36, 38*
• Haman's attempts	*Est 3*

New Testament Stratagems

• Joseph's fears:	*Matt 1*
• Herod's attempts:	*Matt 2*
• At Nazareth:	*Luke 4*
• 2 storms on the Sea:	*Mark 4; Luke 8*
• The Cross	
• Summary:	*Rev 12*
…and he's not through...	

No Other Equivalents

- Islam's *Koran*
- Hindu's *Veda*
- *Bhagavad-Gita*
- *Book of Mormon*
- Nostradamas' *Centuries*
- Occultic mediums, channelers, "New Age" spirit guides, etc.

Major Prophetic Themes

- Israel
- Jerusalem
- Temple
- Babylon
- Russia (Magog)
- Rise of China
- European Super State
- Ecumenical Religion
- Global Government
- Rise of the Occult

Learn the Bible in 24 Hours: Session 13

Hour 13: How Sure Can We Be? (Intro to the New Testament)

1) Approximately how many predictions are there in the Bible?

2) Why is the Septuagint Translation of the Old Testament significant to the New Testament reader?

3) List the eight exemplar prophecies and summarize each of their fulfillments.

4) Why are the *a priori* estimates of each of the candidate prophecies used in the session *not* critical? (Use your own estimates and calculate the result.) How would prophecies that are *more* technical (or specific) alter the result?

Group Discussion Questions: See *Small Group Leaders* section of this workbook.

Preparation for the Next Session:

Familiarize yourself with the books that make up the New Testament.

Learn the Bible
in 24 Hours
Hour Fourteen
The New Testament

The New Testament

Historical Books		5
The Gospels	4	
Acts	1	
Interpretive Letters		21
Paul's Epistles	14*	
Hebrew Christian Epistles	7	
The Revelation		1
(*some argue Paul's authorship of Hebrews)		27

The New Testament

- The Old Testament compiled over several thousand years;
- The New Testament compiled within one lifetime:
  - Four Gospels (Luke in two volumes)
  - Pauline Corpus (and other epistles)
  - Circulated with LXX for instruction & worship
- Luke & Paul *rely* on contemporary eye-witnesses

Conspicuous NT Omissions

- Nero's persecutions after 64 AD
- Execution of James, 62 AD
- Jewish Revolt against Romans, 66 AD
- Destruction of Jerusalem, 70 AD

Syntactic Peculiarities in NT

- Semitic sentence structure: Hebrew more likely than Aramaic
- Mark quotes Luke in hundreds of places
- Mark quotes Acts in 150 places
- Mark knew Thessalonians, Corinthians, Romans, Colossians, James
- 600 evidences of early date of Luke

David Flusser, Hebrew University; Robert Lindsey

The Jerusalem School

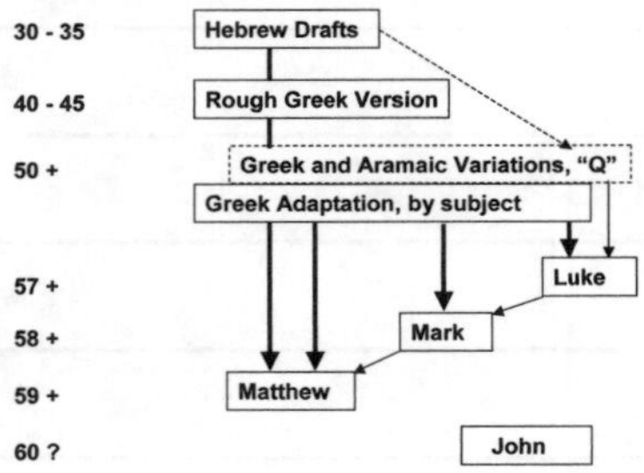

Paul's Letters

Thessalonians	Spring 50; 50-51
1 Corinthians	Spring 55
1 Timothy	Fall 55
2 Corinthians	Spring 56
Galatians	Fall 56
Romans	Spring 57
Titus	Fall 57
Philippians	Summer 58
Colossians	Summer 58
Ephesians	Summer 58
2 Timothy	Fall 58

John A.T. Robinson

Other NT Books

James	47 – 48
Jude	61 – 61
Peter	61 – 62
Acts	57 – 62
1, 2, 3 John	60 – 65
1 Peter	Spring 65
Gospels	40 – 65

John A.T. Robinson

Textus Receptus

- End of 3rd century, Lucian of Antioch compiled Greek text to become primary standard throughout Byzantine world.
- 6th – 14th century majority of NT texts produced in Byzantium in Greek.
- 1525: Erasmus, using 5 or 6 Byzantine manuscripts, compiled first Greek text produced on printing press. Basis for TR.

English Bible

- 1382 Wycliffe Bible (from Vulgate)
- 1525 Erasmus' NT (Greek; TR basis)
- 1526 Tyndale Bible (1st English NT)
- 1534 Luther's Bible (1st German)
- 1535 Coverdale's (1st complete)
- 1537 Matthew Bible (from Tyndale's notes)
- 1539 Great Bible (Coverdale's revision)
- 1560 Geneva Bible (Whittingham, et al)
- 1568 Bishop's Bible (Revised "Great Bible")
- 1609 Douay/Rheims Bible (Vulgate rendering)
- 1611 King James Version

King James Version

- James VI of Scotland becomes King of England (known as "James I")
- 1607: More than 50 scholars, thru prayerful committees
- 5556 manuscripts available; major reliance on *Textus Receptus*
- Heralded as "the noblest monument of English prose."

The Alexandrian Codices

- Codex Alexandrinus
  - About 1630, Codex Alexandrinus was brought to England. A fifth century manuscript containing the entire New Testament.
- Codex Siniaticus
  - 200 years later, a German scholar name Constantin von Tischendorf discovered the Codex Sinaiticus in St. Catherine's Monastery at (the traditional) Mt. Sinai. This manuscript, dated around 350 AD, is one of the two oldest manuscripts of the Greek New Testament.
- Codex Vaticanus
  - had been in the Vatican Library since at least 1481, but was not made available to scholars until the middle of the 19th century. Dated slightly earlier (325 AD) than Codex Sinaiticus, is regarded by many as one of the most reliable copies of the Greek New Testament.

(These have become controversial for a number of reasons.)

Textus Receptus Dethroned

- 1730's: Johannes Albert Bengel, produced a text that deviated from the *Textus Receptus* relying on the earlier manuscripts.
- 1831: Karl Lachman, produced a text that represented the 4th century manuscripts.
- 1857-72: Samuel Tregelles, self-taught in Latin, Hebrew and Greek, spent his lifetime in publishing a Greek text that came out–in six parts–from 1857 to 1872.

Westcott & Hort

- Brooke Foss Westcott and Fenton John Anthony Hort were Anglican churchmen who had contempt for the *Textus Receptus*.
- They began a work in 1853 that resulted, after 28 years, in a Greek New Testament, based on the corrupt *Vaticanus* and *Siniaticus*.
- Both were influenced by Origen and others who denied the deity of Jesus Christ and embraced the prevalent Gnostic heresies of the period from the headquarters of the Gnostics, Alexandria.
- There are over 3,000 contradictions in the four gospels alone between these manuscripts. They changed the traditional Greek text in 8,413 places.

History of the English Bible

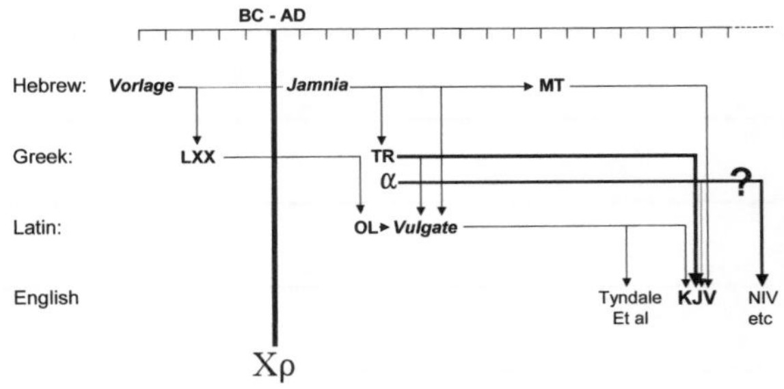

Why we accept the Bible

- The authentication of Christ
  - LXX: over 300 detailed specifications
  - Daniel "70 Weeks" undeniable
- The authentication by Christ
  - The Torah
  - Daniel, et al
- Integrated Design
  - Transcendental Origin

Hidden Authentication Codes

- Microcodes
- Macrocodes
  - Genesis 5
  - Genesis 22
  - Ruth
  - Joshua
- Transcendent Numerical Design

How can *You* know?

- John 7:17

  If any man will do his will, he shall know of the doctrine, whether it be of God, or whether I speak of myself

Learn the Bible in 24 Hours: Session 14

Hour 14: The New Testament (How We Got our Bible)

1) Compare the organization of the New Testament books with those of the Old Testament: historical, interpretive, and prophetic.

2) Contrast the origins of the New Testament with that of the Old Testament.

3) List the conspicuous *omissions* that imply an early date of the New Testament manuscripts.

4) Summarize the origin of *Textus Receptus* and its significance today.

5) Why are the Alexandrian Codices controversial?

6) Why have works of Westcott & Hort become controversial?

7) List the primary reasons that we can accept the current English Bible(s) with confidence.

8) Sketch a time line of the history of the English Bible.

Group Discussion Questions: See *Small Group Leaders* section of this workbook.

Preparation for the Next Session:

Familiarize yourself with the four Gospels.

Learn the Bible
in 24 Hours
Hour Fifteen
The Gospels

"He Shall Glorify Me" John 16:14

- Old Testament
  - Christ in Prophecy — "Behold, He Comes!"
- Gospels
  - Christ in History — "Behold, He Dies!"
- Acts
  - Christ in the Church — "Behold, He Lives!"
- Epistles
  - Christ in Experience — "Behold, He Saves!"
- Apocalypse
  - Christ in coming Glory — "Behold, He Reigns!"

New Testament

Historical Books - 5
- Matthew
- Mark
- Luke
- John
- Acts

Paul's Epistles - 13
- Romans
- 1, 2 Corinthians
- Galatians
- Ephesians
- Philippians
- Colossians
- 1, 2 Thessalonians
- 1, 2 Timothy
- Titus
- Philemon

Hebrew Epistles - 8
- Hebrews
- James
- 1, 2 Peter
- 1, 2, 3, John
- Jude

Prophetic - 1
- Revelation

The Design of the Gospels

	Matthew	Mark	Luke	John
Presents as:	Messiah	Servant	Son of Man	Son of God
Genealogy:	Abraham (Legal)	--	Adam (Blood line)	Eternal (Preexistence)
What Jesus	Said	Did	Felt	Was
To the:	Jew	Roman	Greek	Church
1st Miracle:	Leper cleansed (Jew = sin)	Demon expelled	Demon expelled	Water to Wine
Ends with	Resurrection	Ascension	Promise of Spirit: Acts	Promise of Return: Revelation
Camp Side:	East	West	South	North
Ensign:	Judah	Ephraim	Reuben	Dan
Face:	**Lion**	**Ox**	**Man**	**Eagle**
Style:	Groupings	Snapshots	Narrative	Mystical

The Gospel of Matthew

The Lion of Judah

- Introduction
  - Genealogy, Baptism, Temptations 1-4
- The Galilean Ministry
  - The Tenfold Message 5-8
  - The Ten Miracles 8-10
  - The Ten Rejections 11-18
- The Climax in Judea
  - Presentation as King 19-25
  - The Crucifixion 26-27
  - The Resurrection 28

Major Discourses

- Sermon on the Mount Matt 5 – 8
  - Moral standards; motives
- Olivet Discourse Matt 24, 25
  - Second Coming
- The Kingdom Parables Matt 13

The Seven Kingdom Parables

Matthew 13	Revelation 2, 3
• The Sower and 4 Soils	Ephesus
• The Tares and the Wheat	Smyrna
• The Mustard Seed	Pergamos
• The Woman and the Leaven	Thyatira
• The Treasure in the Field	Sardis
• The Pearl of Great Price	Philadelphia
• The Dragnet	Laodicea

Mark

- No nativity narrative or genealogy
- Longer than Matthew
  - (excluding discourses)
- Graphic perspective of an eyewitness
  - Names, times, numbers, locations
- Peter's amanuensis
  - Translated from Aramaic

The Gospel of Mark
The Suffering Servant

- Four Voices Announce 1
- The Mighty Works 2-8
  - 12 selected and sent
- The Coming Climax 8-15
  - Transfiguration
  - Final Week
- Finale 16
  - Resurrection; Ascension

Luke

- Most complete narrative
  - Over 20 miracles (6 unique)
  - 23 parables (18 unique)
- Authenticated historian, writer
- A Gentile; a Physician
- Luke I & II ("Gospel" + "Acts")
  - Sponsored by Theophilus
  - Support for Paul's appeal to Caesar?

The Gospel of Luke

The Son of Man

- The Incarnation 1-3
  - Two annunciations;
  - Two elect mothers
  - Two anticipated births
- The Galilean Ministry 4-9
  - Teachings, miracles, 12 sent
- The Journey toward Jerusalem 10-19
- The Heir Executed 19-24
  - Presented riding a donkey
  - Passover, Gethsemane, Golgatha

Seven Crises of Christ

- His Birth
- His Baptism
- His Temptation
- His Transfiguration
- His Crucifixion
- His Resurrection
- His Ascension

G. Campbell Morgan

The Gospel of John
The Son of God

- Prologue
  - The Word became Flesh 1
- Public Ministry to the Jews
  - Signs, Declarations, Conflicts 2-12
- Private Ministry to "His Own"
  - Presages: Departure, Coming Spirit 13-17
- Tragedy and Triumph
  - Apprehension and prosecution 18
  - Crucifixion and Burial 19
  - Resurrection 20
- Epilogue: "Till I come" 21

Eight Miracles

- Turning Water into Wine 2
- Healing Nobleman's son 4
- Curing of Bethesda paralytic 5
- Feeding the 5,000 6
- Walking on the Sea 6
- Sight to the Blind man 9
- Raising of Lazarus 11
- Draught of fishes 21

In Retrospect

- Matthew
  - The Promised One is here; see His Credentials
- Mark
  - This is how He worked; see His Power
- Luke
  - This is what He was like; see His Nature
- John
  - This is who He really was; see His Godship

"I AM that I AM"

Exodus 3:14

- I AM the Bread of Life 6:35,41,48,51
- I AM the Light of the World 8:12
- I AM the Door of the Sheep 10:7,9
- I AM the Good Shepherd 10:11, 14
- I AM the Resurrection and Life 11:25
- I AM the Way, the Truth, the Life 14:6
- I AM the True Vine 15:1, 5

Tabernacle Furniture

• Brazen Altar	Atonement
• Brazen Laver	Regeneration
• Table of Shewbread	Living Bread
• Lampstand	Light of the World
• Altar of Incense	Intercession
• Ark of the Covenant	Covenant Access
• Mercy Seat	Propitiation

Chronology

- Tiberius appointed: 14 AD
  - Augustus died August 19, 14 AD
- (Within the) 15th year of Tiberius Luke 3:1
- Thus, ministry began in fall 28 AD
- 4th Passover: April 6, 32 AD
  Sir Robert Anderson's dating
- Other chronologies assume a Friday crucifixion

Learn the Bible in 24 Hours: Session 15

Hour 15: The Gospels (Matthew, Mark, Luke, John)

1) Contrast the role of the Gospels with a) The Old Testament b) The Epistles of the New Testament c) The Book of Revelation.

2) Contrast the four Gospels with respect to: a) Principal focus and supporting details b) Genealogical presentation c) Stylistic distinctives d) Closing emphasis

3) Which of the Gospel writers was skilled in shorthand writing? How is that significant?

4) Which of the Gospels is most like a shooting script for a movie? Give examples.

5) Which of the Gospels emphasize the Galilean ministry? Which of the Gospels emphasize the Judean ministry?

6) What are seven primary crises in the life of Christ?

7) Where do we find the seven "I AM" statements of Christ? Why?

Group Discussion Questions: See *Small Group Leaders* section of this workbook.

Preparation for the Next Session:

Review the narrative of the Final Week of Christ in each of the four Gospels.

Learn the Bible

in 24 Hours

Hour Sixteen

The Final Week

Final Week

Friday	At Bethany	John 12:1
Saturday	Triumphal Entry	Matt 21:5, 12,17; Mark 11:7, 11; Luke 19:28
Sunday	The Fig tree cursed	Matt 21:18; Mark 11:12
Monday	Conspirators counsel	Matt 26:2; Mark 11:20; Mark 14:1; Luke 22:1
Tuesday	Last Supper *"between the evenings"*	Matt 26:17; Mark 14:7, 12; Luke 22:7
Wednesday	Crucifixion	John 19:14,31,42;; Mark 15:42; Luke 23:17,54
Thursday	Feast of Unleavened Bread	Lev 23:4-8
Friday	Women prepare spices	
Saturday	"…and rested…" *"after the Sabbaths.."*	Luke 23:56; Matt 28:1
Sunday	He is risen!	Matt 28:11; Mark 16:1; Luke 24:1; John 20:1

The 69 Weeks

of Daniel 9

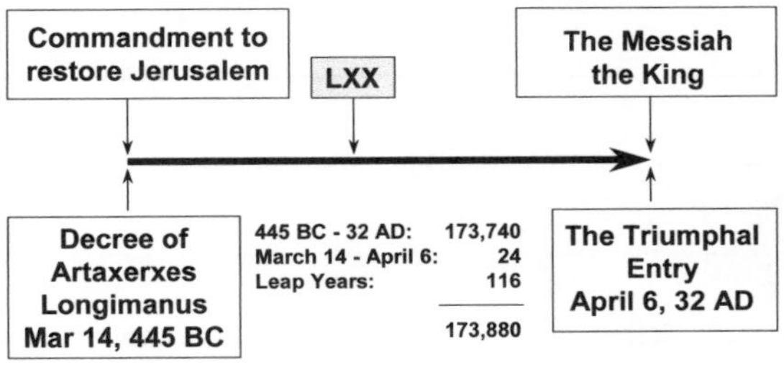

The Interval

(not to scale)

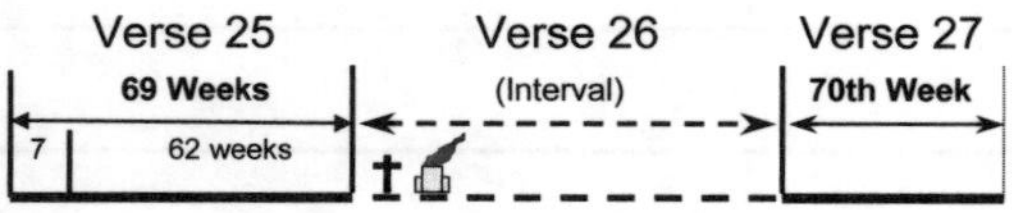

Six Trials

- Jewish Trials
  - Before Annas
  - Before Caiaphas
  - Before the Sanhedrin
- Roman Trials
  - Before Pilate
  - Before Herod
  - Before Pilate

Pilate's Attempts

- Pronounced innocent by the personal representative of the ruler of the world.
- Pass-off to Herod
- Pass-off to the crowd…
- Holiday gesture: Prisoner of choice released
  - Barabbas or "your king"?

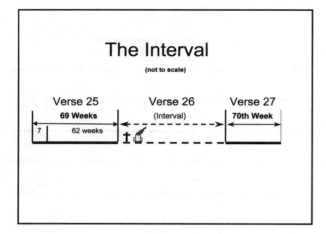

Mutual Exchange of Positions

- Barabbas is installed in all the rights and privileges of Jesus Christ;
- while the latter enters upon all the infamy and horror of the rebel's position.
- The delinquent's guilt and cross become the lot of the Just One, and
- all the civil rights and immunities of the later are the property of the delinquent.

Topology of Mount Moriah

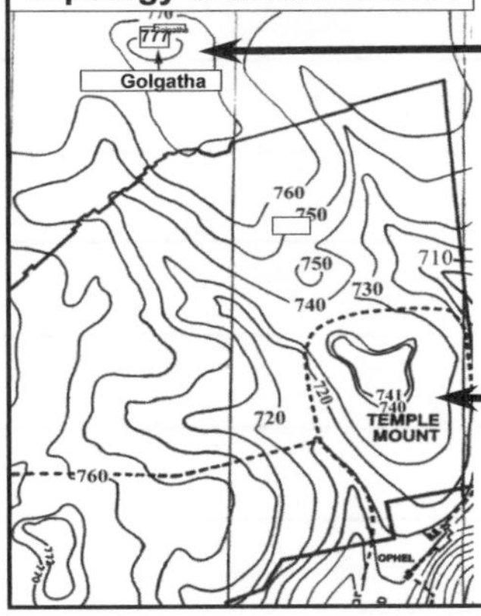

Peak: Akedah

Threshing Floor of Arunah

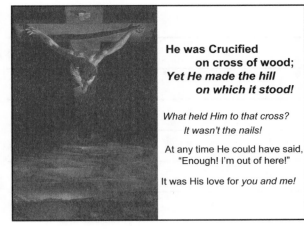

He was Crucified
on cross of wood;
Yet He made the hill
on which it stood!

What held Him to that cross?
It wasn't the nails!

At any time He could have said,
"Enough! I'm out of here!"

It was His love for *you and me!*

The Resurrection

New Beginnings

Crucified on the 14th of Nisan;

In the grave: _3_ days;

Resurrection: 17th of Nisan ("7th month")

God's "new beginning" on the Planet Earth was on the anniversary—in anticipation—of our "new beginning" in Christ!

Post-Resurrection Appearances

• Mary Magdalene, early Sun morning	Mark 16:9-10
• Other Women, early Sun morning	Matt 28:9-10
• Two on Emmaus Rd, Sun afternoon	Luke 24:13-32
• Peter, sometime that day	Luke 24:34
• Eleven, that night (w/o Thomas)	Luke 24:36ff
• Eleven, a week later (with Thomas)	John 20:26-31
• Seven, Galilean breakfast	John 21
• Eleven, in Galilee	Matt 28:16-20
• 500, in Galilee	1 Corinth 15:6
• James	1 Corinth 15:7
• Final Appearance & Ascension	Luke 24:44f
• Paul, on the Damascus Road	Acts 9:3-7

Why Wasn't He Recognized?

- Mary in the Garden? John 20:11-16
- On the Emmaus Road? Luke 24:13-32
- In the Upper Room? Luke 24:33-43
- By the Sea of Galilee? John 21:3-12

Old Testament Descriptions

- Psalm 22
- Isaiah 53
  - Isaiah 52:14
- Isaiah 50:6
- Zechariah 12:10

An Additional Detail

"I gave my back to the smiters,
and my cheeks to them that plucked off the hair:
I hid not my face from shame and spitting."

Isaiah 50:6

Zechariah 12:10

...and they shall look upon me
(את) whom they have pierced,...

וְשָׁפַכְתִּי עַל־בֵּית דָּוִיד וְעַל יוֹשֵׁב יְרוּשָׁלִַם
רוּחַ חֵן וְתַחֲנוּנִים וְהִבִּיטוּ אֵלַי אֵת
אֲשֶׁר־דָּקָרוּ וְסָפְדוּ עָלָיו כְּמִסְפֵּד עַל־הַיָּחִיד
וְהָמֵר עָלָיו כְּהָמֵר עַל־הַבְּכוֹר׃

New Testament Preview

And I beheld, and, lo, in the midst of the throne and of the four living creatures, and in the midst of the elders,
stood ***the Lamb as it had been slain...***
Revelation 5:6

The Next Phase

"...It is expedient for you that I go away: for if I go not away,
the Comforter will not come unto you; but if I depart, I will send him unto you."
John 16:7

Learn the Bible in 24 Hours: Session 16

Hour 16: The Final Week

1) Explain three texts in the Gospels that appear to argue *against* a Friday Crucifixion.

2) Why do some believe that the 4th Passover in Christ's ministry was in A.D. 32?

3) List the major events in the Final Week of Christ, with Scripture references.

4) Sketch a timeline explaining Luke 19 in terms of Daniel 9. *Why* was Jerusalem destroyed in A.D. 70?

5) List four attempts of Pilate to "get off the hook."

6) In what way are *we* in Barabbas' shoes?

7) Link the geography, and the significances, of Golgatha with Abrahm's offering of Isaac (Genesis 22).

8) Compare, on the Jewish calendar, the Resurrection with the end of the Flood of Noah (Genesis 8:4). How might this be significant?

9) List the post-resurrection appearances of Christ, with references.

Group Discussion Questions: See *Small Group Leaders* section of this workbook.

Preparation for the Next Session:

Read the Book of Acts.

Learn the Bible
in 24 Hours
Hour Seventeen
Acts

Acts (of the Holy Spirit)

• Ascension	1
• Pentecost – Birth of the Church	2
• Outrage against Stephen	7
• Philip & Ethiopian Treasurer	8
• Call of Paul	9
• Peter's Vision at Cornelius'	10
• Mission to Gentiles	11-14
• Council at Jerusalem	15

Acts (Continued)

• 1st Missionary Journey	13, 14
• 2nd Missionary Journey	15
– Athens, Mars Hill	17
• 3rd Missionary Journey	18
• Outcry against Paul	22
– Before Sanhedrin	23
– Before Governor Felix	24
– Before Governor Festus	25
– Before King Agrippa	26
• Paul goes to Rome	27-28

Parallels

1 - 12	13 - 28
Jerusalem the Center	Antioch the Center
Peter the Chief figure	Paul the chief figure
Out to Samaria	Out to Rome
Word rejected by Jews of homeland	Word rejected by Jews of Dispersion
Peter imprisoned	Paul imprisoned
Judgment on Herod	Judgment on Jews

Parallels

Peter		Paul	
First Sermon	2	First Sermon	13
Lame Man healed	3	Lame man healed	14
Simon the Sorcerer	8	Elymas the sorcerer	13
Influence of shadow	5	Influence of handkerchief	19
Laying on of hands	8	Laying on of hands	19
Peter worshipped	10	Paul worshipped	14
Tabitha raised	9	Eutychus raised	20
Peter imprisoned	12	Paul imprisoned	28

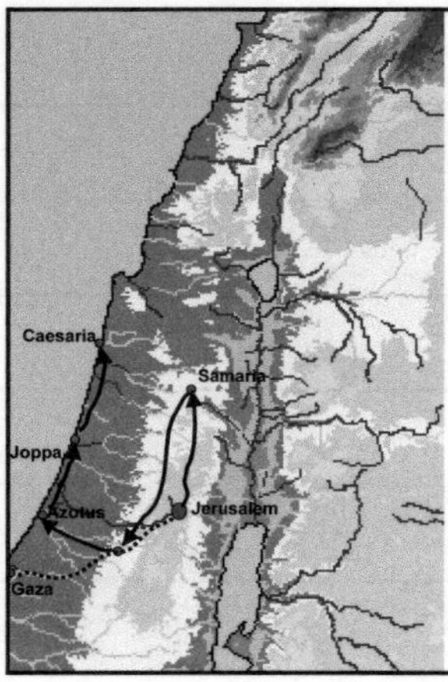

Acts of Philip

Philip goes to Samaria — Acts 8:5
Many are healed
Simon the Magician believes — Acts 8:9f
Peter and John investigate — Acts 8:14
Return after admonishing Simon

Philip is sent to the Jerusalem-Gaza Road
Meets the Ethiopian Treasurer — Acts 8:26f

Peter travels north, preaching in every town — Acts 8:40

Peter settles in Caesarea with wife and Daughters — Acts 21:8

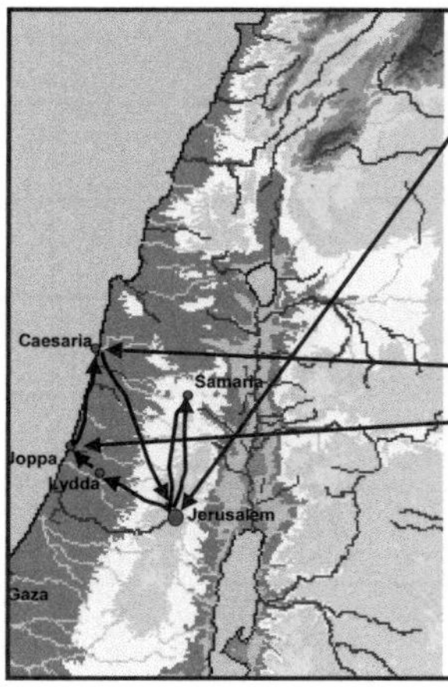

Acts of Peter

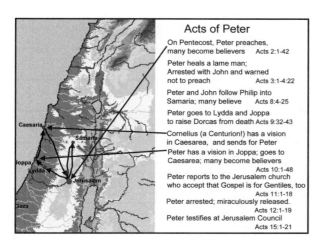

On Pentecost, Peter preaches, many become believers Acts 2:1-42

Peter heals a lame man; Arrested with John and warned not to preach Acts 3:1-4:22

Peter and John follow Philip into Samaria; many believe Acts 8:4-25

Peter goes to Lydda and Joppa to raise Dorcas from death Acts 9:32-43

Cornelius (a Centurion!) has a vision in Caesarea, and sends for Peter

Peter has a vision in Joppa; goes to Caesarea; many become believers Acts 10:1-48

Peter reports to the Jerusalem church who accept that Gospel is for Gentiles, too Acts 11:1-18

Peter arrested; miraculously released. Acts 12:1-19

Peter testifies at Jerusalem Council Acts 15:1-21

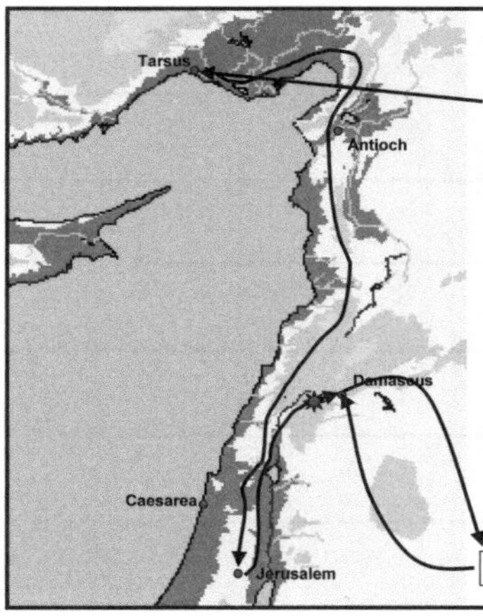

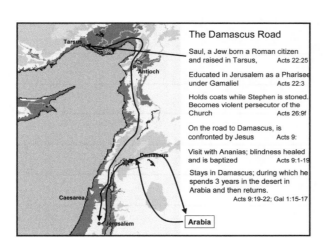

The Damascus Road

Saul, a Jew born a Roman citizen and raised in Tarsus, Acts 22:25

Educated in Jerusalem as a Pharisee under Gamaliel Acts 22:3

Holds coats while Stephen is stoned. Becomes violent persecutor of the Church Acts 26:9f

On the road to Damascus, is confronted by Jesus Acts 9:

Visit with Ananias; blindness healed and is baptized Acts 9:1-19

Stays in Damascus; during which he spends 3 years in the desert in Arabia and then returns. Acts 9:19-22; Gal 1:15-17

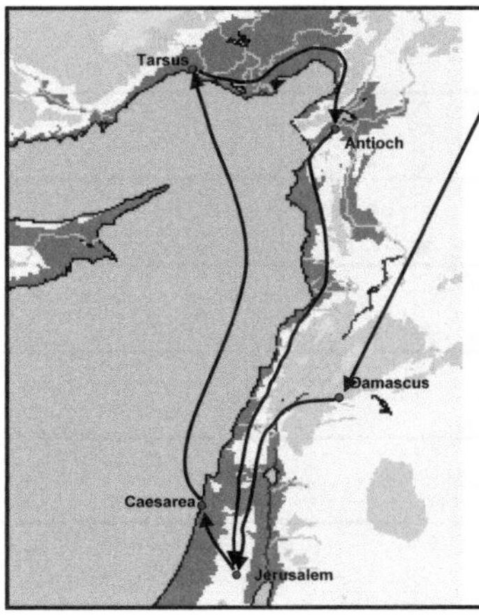

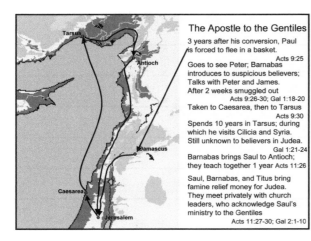

The Apostle to the Gentiles

3 years after his conversion, Paul is forced to flee in a basket. Acts 9:25

Goes to see Peter; Barnabas introduces to suspicious believers; Talks with Peter and James. After 2 weeks smuggled out Acts 9:26-30; Gal 1:18-20

Taken to Caesarea, then to Tarsus Acts 9:30

Spends 10 years in Tarsus; during which he visits Cilicia and Syria. Still unknown to believers in Judea. Gal 1:21-24

Barnabas brings Saul to Antioch; they teach together 1 year Acts 11:26

Saul, Barnabas, and Titus bring famine relief money for Judea. They meet privately with church leaders, who acknowledge Saul's ministry to the Gentiles Acts 11:27-30; Gal 2:1-10

1st Missionary Journey

13 - 14

- Salamis 13:5
- Paphos 13:6
- Antioch (Pisidia) 13:14
- Iconium 13:51
- Lystra and Derbe 14:6, 20
- Return journey 14:21, 22

The Council in Jerusalem

- Considerable controversy erupts over the obligations incumbent upon Gentile believers.
  - Circumcision?
  - Keeping the Mosaic Law, etc.
- Paul, Barnabas, and others seek the elders in Jerusalem for resolution.
- Peter also testifies…

The *Two* Problems Raised

1. What must a Gentile do to be saved?
2. What is to become of Israel?

The Resolution(s)

- Gentiles should:
  - Abstain from idols
  - Abstain from fornication
  - Abstain from things strangled, and blood;
- [No commitment to Mosaic practices]
  - Ceremonial laws
  - Circumcision, etc.
- The issue of Israel's destiny
  - Romans 9, 10, 11

2nd Missionary Journey

15:36 – 18:22

- Philippi
- Thessalonica
- Berea
- Athens
- Corinth
- Ephesus

Paul on Mars Hill

Aeropagus: Court of the Judges

Paul begins where the people were:

Their idolatry (30,000 “gods”)

You are "extremely devout"; "very god-fearing"

The altar to the Unknown God:

"We are his offspring...:

astronomical poem of Aratus,

Greek countryman of Paul's (his precedessor by 300 yrs)

religious hymn of Cleanthes of Troas

a contemporary of Aratus;

[Paul also quoted Menander in I Cor 15:33]

Paul's Hearings

- Before Sanhedrin 23
  - Arguments turn to violence
- Before Governor Felix 24
  - Defers. After 2 years, Festus replaces Felix
- Before Governor Festus 25
  - "I appeal to Caesar"
- Before King Agrippa 26
  - While awaiting his appeal

Paul's Final Footprints

The Pastoral Letters

- 1 Timothy
  - Released from house arrest in Rome, Paul heading for Macedonia,having left Timothy in Ephesus to continue the work 1 Tim 1:3
- Titus
  - Having left Titus in Crete, Paul plans to meet up at Nicopolis en route from Crete to Dalmatia. Titus 3:12; 2 Tim 4:10
- 2 Timothy
  - From prison in Rome having been re-arrested, and expecting execution soon. His final letter. 2 Tim 4:13, 16-17
- Visit to Spain? Rom 15:24, 28

The Book of Acts

- The Birth of the Church
  - As distinct from Israel
- The Gateway to the Epistles
  - Interpretation and Significances
- History of the first 30 years of the Church
  (Revelation 2 & 3: the next two thousand…)

Learn the Bible in 24 Hours: Session 17

Hour 17: The Book of Acts

1) Make a list of the key chapters in Acts, focusing on a) Peter (in the 1st half) and b) Paul (in the second half). c) How are their respective ministries similar? How are they different?

2) Sketch a map of the Mediterranean on a separate piece of paper and include the key events in Paul's a) 1st Missionary Journey b) 2nd Missionary Journey c) Final voyage to Rome.

3) What *two* issues were aired at the Council of Jerusalem? How do they impact our *prophetic* understanding?

4) Summarize Paul's four hearings

a) Before the Sanhedrin
b) Before Governor Felix
c) Before Governor Festus
d) Before King Agrippa

Group Discussion Questions: See *Small Group Leaders* section of this workbook.

Preparation for the Next Session:

Read Paul's definitive statement of Christian doctrine: The Book of Romans.

Learn the Bible
in 24 Hours
Hour Eighteen
Romans

The Epistle to the Romans

- The Definitive Gospel According to Paul
  - Most comprehensive book in the NT
- Impact on History: *unequaled!*
  - Grace gradually erodes to forms of legalism...
  - When grace becomes obscured:
    - 590-1517 = "The Dark Ages"
    - *The Kingdom of Blood*, a history of the church

Outline of Romans
The Gospel According to Paul

• Doctrinal:	**Faith**	1 - 8
– Sin: (the most complete diagnosis)		1-3
– Salvation		4-5
– Sanctification		6-8
• Dispensational:	**Hope**	9-11
– Israel - Past		9
– Israel - Present		10
– Israel - Future		11
• Practical:	**Love**	12-16

Section 1: Doctrinal

- Introduction
  - The Plight of Pagan Man 1:1-32
  - The Moral Man 2:1-16
  - The Religious Man 2:17-29
- God's Greatest Problem 3
- God's Greatest Gift 4
- The Peace of God 5
- The Death of Defeat 6
- Law School 7
- The Security We Have in Christ 8

Three Tenses of "*Being Saved*"

- *Have been saved*: From the ***penalty*** of sin;
  - Positionally, Eph 2:8, 9
  - Called *justification salvation.*
- *Are being saved*: From the ***power*** of sin;
  - Operationally, by the Holy Spirit, moment-by-moment; Rom 6
  - Called *sanctification.*
- *Shall be saved*: From the ***presence*** of sin;
  - Called, "the redemption of our body." Rom 8:23

Why Was the Law Given?

Romans 7

1. Law was given to expose our sin nature; 7:7
2. To incite the sin nature to sin more 7:8-23

   Sin nature cannot be reformed
3. To drive us to despair of self-effort 7:24, 25
4. To drive us to dependence upon the Holy Spirit alone 8:1-4

Law vs. Spirit

Depends on the flesh	Rom 8:3
Depends upon God's power	Luke 23:49; Acts 1:8
Produces rebellion	Rom 7:8
Produces God's desires	Phil 2:13
Results in more sin	Rom 5:20
Righteousness	Rom 8:4
Brings wrath	Rom 4:15
Brings joy, peace, production	Gal 5:22, 23
Not of faith	Gal 3:12
By faith	Gal 5:5; 2 Cor 5:7
Kills	2 Cor 3:4-6; Gal 3:21
Gives life...	

Romans 8

- Deliverance from the flesh
  by the power of the Holy Spirit. 8:1-11
- Realization of our Sonship
  by the Holy Spirit's inner witness. 8:12-17
- Preservation in suffering
  by the power of the Holy Spirit 8:18-30
- Hymn of Praise for Victory 8:31-39.
  God's logic of our security

Chapter opens: no possibility of condemnation.

Chapter closes: no possibility of separation!

Chapter 5 vs. Chapter 8

5: A summation of the *saving* work of Jesus Christ;
  8: A summation of what Christ did to *provide Victory*
5: justification (declared righteous) by faith is forever;
  8: godly life is insured through the power of the Holy Spirit.
5: our performance is based on understanding of God's love
  8: our performance is based on the power of the Holy Spirit
5: it reveals our relationship to God;
  8: it reveals our relationship to the world, conflict, the flesh
5: the Holy Spirit is mentioned only once (v.5);
  8: the Holy Spirit is available to us to give us assured victory.
5: is the capstone on our *salvation* in Christ;
  8: is the capstone on our *victory* in Christ.

Why do Christians have trials?

1. To glorify God — Dan 3:16-18, 24-25
2. Discipline for known sin — Heb 12:5-11; James 4:17 Rom 14:23; 1 John 1:9
3. To prevent us from falling into sin — 1 Pet 4:1-2
4. To keep us from Pride
5. To build faith — 1 Pet 1:6-7
6. To cause growth — Rom 5:3-5
7. To teach obedience and discipline — Acts 9:15-16; Phil 4:11-13
8. To equip us to comfort others — 2 Cor 1:3-4
9. To prove the reality of Christ in us — 2 Cor 4:7-11
10. For testimony to the angels — Job 1:8; Eph 3:8-11; 1 Pet 1:12

--Hal Lindsey, *Combat Faith*

Section 2: The Israel Trilogy

Romans 9 - Israel Past
Romans 10 - Israel Present
Romans 11 - Israel Future

[Other chapter "trilogies":]

Sermon on the Mount:	Matthew 5, 6, 7
Spiritual Gifts:	1 Corinthians 12, 13, 14
2nd Coming:	Zechariah 12, 13, 14

The Historical Dilemma

If God is so faithful to His word,
(as portrayed in Romans 8)
that none can be condemned that He has justified; and
that none in Him can be separated;
then why have the Israelites,
who were sovereignly chosen and given unconditional promises,
completely failed and then been rejected?

Whence the Jew?

- So there is also the problem of how the Gentiles are to relate to the Jews.
  - If circumcision is of no value without faith, then what advantage has the Jew?
  - What is the benefit of circumcision?
- (Same question was underlying Acts 15; and will be answered in Romans 9, 10, and 11).
- From Genesis 12 to Acts 2: it's all about Israel...
  ...and that God keeps His promises!
- We need a *doctrinal*, as well as *devotional*, understanding of the Word of God...

The Abrahamic Covenant

1. And I will make of thee a great nation,
2. and I will bless thee,
3. and make thy name great;
4. and thou shalt be a blessing:
5. And I will bless them that bless thee,
6. and curse him that curseth thee:
7. and *in thee shall all families of the earth be blessed.*

Genesis 12:2-3

The Terms of the Covenant

- Declared eternal and unconditional
- Re-confirmed by an oath: Gen 22:15-18
- Confirmed to Isaac and to Jacob: Gen 26:2-5
  (despite acts of disobedience);
- NT declares it immutable: Heb 6:13-18

The Fundamental Promise

- *There is no other such promise to any other people!*
- So how do *we* get <u>*our*</u> benefit from this covenant?
  - We rely entirely on our derivative benefit from the Root of David, the Lion of the Tribe of Judah.

3 "Until's" of Israel

1st condition for restoration:

"*Until* they acknowledge their offence…"

Hosea 5:15

2nd condition for restoration:

"*Until* the Fullness of Gentiles brought in."

Romans 11:25

3rd condition for restoration:

"*Until* the Times of the Gentiles are fulfilled."

Luke 21:24

Section 3: Practical

- Responsibilities from gifts 12
- Civil Responsibilities 13
- Christian Maturity 14
- Unity within the Body 15
- Personal Greetings 16

Learn the Bible in 24 Hours: Session 18

Hour 18: Paul's Definitive Doctrinal Summary (Romans)

1) Outline the major sections and topics in this Epistle.

2) In what way is Romans 1 the "great leveler"?

3) Define God's greatest problem, and how His gift resolves it.

4) Explain the three tenses of "being saved."

5) Why was the Law given?

6) List six contrasts between the "law" and the "Spirit."

7) Contrast "salvation" (Romans 5) with "victory" (Romans 8).

8) List 10 reasons Christians have trials.

9) What is "Replacement Theology" and how is it refuted in Chapters 9, 10, and 11 of Romans?

10) What three conditions remain as a prerequisite to the restoration of Israel?

11) In what way does all of our benefits—as Gentiles—depend upon the Abrahamic Covenant?

Group Discussion Questions: See *Small Group Leaders* section of this workbook.

Preparation for the Next Session:

Read the other "Church Epistles": 1 & 2 Corinthians, Galatians, Ephesians, Philippians, Colossians, 1 & 2 Thessalonians, and the "Pastoral Epistles," 1 & 2 Timothy, Titus and Philemon.

Learn the Bible
in 24 Hours
Hour Nineteen
The Church Epistles

New Testament

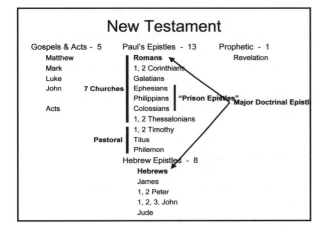

Gospels & Acts - 5
- Matthew
- Mark
- Luke
- John
- Acts

Paul's Epistles - 13
- **7 Churches**
  - **Romans**
  - 1, 2 Corinthians
  - Galatians
  - Ephesians
  - Philippians
  - Colossians
  - 1, 2 Thessalonians
- **"Prison Epistles"**: Ephesians, Philippians, Colossians
- **Pastoral**
  - 1, 2 Timothy
  - Titus
  - Philemon

Hebrew Epistles - 8
- **Hebrews**
- James
- 1, 2 Peter
- 1, 2, 3, John
- Jude

Prophetic - 1
- Revelation

Major Doctrinal Epistl (Romans, Hebrews)

Spiritual Order

Romans	Doctrine	Soteriology (Salvation)
1, 2 Corinthians	Reproof	
Galatians	Correction	
Ephesians	Doctrine	Ecclesiology (Church)
Philippians	Reproof	
Colossians	Correction	
1, 2 Thessalonians	Doctrine	Eschatology ("Last Things")

Corinth

Four Letters & Three Visits

A) When the church was founded

1) The "Previous Letter"

(Household of Chloe visit Paul, with a letter *from* Corinth)

2) "1st Corinthians" ("2nd")

B) The "Painful" visit

3) The "Severe Letter" (Lost...)

(Titus' report: received well.)

4) "2nd Corinthians" ("4th" + fragments?)

C) 3rd visit

1st Epistle to the Corinthians

- Schisms are Wrong 1-6
  - True wisdom vs. the "Foolishness of God"
  - Human teachers are but stewards
- Replies to other problems 7-11
  - Marriage, Meats, Lord's Table, etc
- Spiritual Gifts 12-14
- Resurrection 15

Stewardship

- Salvation vs. Rewards
- Two Foundations:

  Gold, Silver, Precious stones

  vs.

  Wood, Hay, Stubble
  - To be tried by fire
- Inheritances are forfeitable
  - The *Metachoi,* or *Koinonos:* partakers

Spiritual Gifts

1 Corinthians 12 - 14

- The Spirit divides them as He will 12
  - Diversity of Gifts but one Spirit 4-11
  - Diversity of members but one body 12-27
  - Diversity of service but one church 28-31
- They are valueless without Love 13
  - The utter necessity of Love 1-3
  - The moral excellency of Love 4-7
  - The abiding supremacy of Love 8-13
- The greatest of them is prophecy 14
  - It most edifies the Church 1-22
  - It most convinces outsiders 23-28
  - Its use should be orderly 29-40

What is the "Gospel"?

Moreover, brethren, I declare unto you the gospel which I preached unto you, which also ye have received, and wherein ye stand;

By which also ye are saved, if ye keep in memory what I preached unto you, unless ye have believed in vain.

For I delivered unto you first of all that which I also received, how that

1) Christ died for our sins according to the Scriptures;

2) And that he was buried,

3) and that he rose again the third day according to the Scriptures. 1 Corinthians 15:1-4

The Resurrection

1 Corinthians 15

- *Most Important Chapter in the Bible*
- *Jurassic Park* offers a glimpse
  - Basic building blocks are fungible elements
  - Only unique requirement: *information* (DNA)
- Jesus' Resurrection as a model
  - Tangible
  - Hyperdimensional (spacially transcendent)

2nd Epistle to the Corinthians

Christ Our Comfort Amid Trial

- Paul's Account of his Ministry 1-5
  - Motive 1-2
  - Message 3-5
- Paul's Appeal to his Converts 6-9
  - Things Spiritual 6, 7
  - Things Material 8, 9
- Paul's Answer to his Critics 10-13
  - Critics and their pretensions
  - The Apostle and his credentials

The Epistle to the Galatians

Liberation Through the Gospel

- Authenticity of the Gospel 1, 2
  - Genuine as to its origin 1
  - Genuine as to its nature 2
- Superiority of the Gospel 3, 4
  - The new relation it effects 3
  - The privileges it releases 4
- The True Liberty of the Gospel 5, 6
  - Love-service ends Law-bondage 5:1-15
  - Spirit ends flesh-bondage 5:16-6:10

The Epistle to the Ephesians

The Great Mystery Revealed

- Our Wealth in Christ 1 – 3
  - Praise for spiritual possession 1:3-14
  - Prayer for spiritual perceptions 1:15-23
  - Our new condition in Christ 2:1-10
  - Our new relation in Christ 2:11-22
  - Revealing of the Divine Mystery 3:1-12
  - Receiving of the Divine Fullness 3:13-21
- Our Walk in Christ 4 – 6
  - Church corporately 4:1-16
  - Believers individually 4:17-5:2
  - Sensual-living outsiders 5:3-21
  - Special Relationships 5:22-6:9
  - The Armor of God 6:10-20

The Epistle to the Colossians

- Doctrinal: The Fullness of Christ 1 –2
  - In the Creation 1:15-18
  - In Redemption 1:19-23
  - In the Church 1:24-2:7
  - Versus Heresy 2:8-23
- Practical: The New Life 3 – 4
  - Believers individually 3:1-11
  - Believers reciprocally 3:12-17
  - Domestic relationships 3:18-21
  - Employment obligations 3:22-4:1
  - Outsiders 4:1-6

  Personal Addenda 4:7-22

1st Epistle to the Thessalonians

- Culmination of the Church Epistles
- Reminiscent in style: *reminds* them of what Paul had taught them in their initial few weeks of teaching
- The *Harpazo*, the "Rapture"

1st Epistle to Timothy

The Local Church and its Minister

- A Charge: Guard the Deposit 1
- The Assembly and Its Conduct 2 – 3
  - Concerning Order 2
    - Men and Public Prayer
    - Women and Public Mien
  - Concerning Office 3
    - Qualification of Elders
    - Qualification of Deacons
- The Minister and His Conduct 4 – 6
  - To the Assembly in General 4
  - To Particular Groups 5, 6

2nd Epistle to Timothy

A Challenge to Faithfulness

- The True Pastor under Testings 1, 2
  - The True Personal Reaction
  - The True Pastoral Reaction
- The True Pastor and End-time Troubles 3, 4
  - The True Personal Reaction
  - The True Pastoral Reaction

Titus

Maintain Good Works

- As to Elders in the Assembly 1
  - Put things in order
- As to Classes in Particular 2
  - Adorn the doctrine
- As to Members in General 3
  - Maintain good works

Philemon

A Personal Intercession

- Salutation 1-3
- Praise of Philemon 4-7
- Plea for Onesimus 8-17
- Paul's Pledge & Assurance 18-22
- Benediction 23-25

Learn the Bible in 24 Hours: Session 19

Hour 19: Paul's Church and Pastoral Epistles

1) List the major categories of New Testament Epistles, and the members of each.

2) Which two are regarded as the primary *doctrinal* epistles? Explain.

3) Which are the "prison epistles"? How is this known?

4) Which are the epistles that deal with: a) Soteriology (salvation)? b) Ecclesiology (the Church)? c) Eschatology ("Last Things")?

5) Summarize the four letters (and three visits) Paul made to Corinth.

6) Summarize the Spiritual Gifts in Chapters 12, 13, & 14 in Paul's 1st letter to Corinth.

7) What is the *definition* of the "Gospel"?

8) What is the most important chapter in the Bible? Why?

9) Which are the most important *prophetic* epistles? Why?

10) What secret was revealed in the Letter to the Ephesians that was hidden from view in the Old Testament?

11) What are the different elements of the "Armor of God"?

Group Discussion Questions: See *Small Group Leaders* section of this workbook.

Preparation for the Next Session:

Read the "Hebrew Epistles": Hebrews, James, (1 & 2) Peter, (1, 2, &3) John, and Jude.

Learn the Bible
in 24 Hours
Hour Twenty

The Hebrew Epistles

The Epistle to the Hebrews
Christ: The New and Living Way

- Jesus: The New and Better Deliverer 1-7
  - The God-man: better than the Angels 1, 2
  - An Apostle better than Moses 3
  - A Leader better than Joshua 4:1-13
  - A Priest better than Aaron 4:14-17
- Calvary: A New and Better Covenant 8-9:18
  - Offers better Promises
  - Opens a better Sanctuary
  - Sealed by a better Sacrifice
  - Achieves far better Results
- Faith: The True and Better Response 9:19-23
  - Parting words 13:22-25

Son's Superiority: His Deity
Hebrews 1:4-14

- Son's position unique Psalm 2:7
- Son head of Davidic Covenant 2 Sam 7:14
- Angels worship the Son Psalm 97:7
- Angels serve the Son Psalm 104:4
- Son to rule the Kingdom Psalm 45:7-8
- Son is the Creator Ps 102:25-27
- Son enthroned at the right hand of God Psalm 110:1

Son's Superiority: His Humanity

Hebrews 2:5-9

- Sovereignty over Earth promised to man, not angels Gen 1:26, 27
- God gave man dominion over earth Psalm 8:5-7
- Man lost it through sin to Satan and his angels
- Messiah regained dominion for Man
  - Man will be associated with Him in rule

Son's Superiority: His Salvation

Hebrews 2:10-18

- To manifest divine grace 2:10-13
  (Citing Psalm 22:22; Isaiah 8:17-18)
- To overcome the Prince of Death 2:14
- To free the believer from fear of death 2:15
- To help man 2:16-18

Responsibility of the Believer

- To produce works which accompany salvation 6:9-12
- Illustration from nature 6:7-8
  - Rain falls on all the earth (believers)
  - Some produce fruit; some do not.
  - Fruitfulness will be rewarded; Fruitlessness will be judged.
  - Thorns and thistles burned; *the land isn't.* 1 Cor 3:10-15

A Better Covenant

Hebrews 8:1-13

- Mosaic Covenant destined to be replaced by a superior one Jer 31:31-34
- The New Covenant
  - Better Promises
  - Better Priesthood
  - Better Sanctuary
  - Better Sacrifice

Contrasts

Levitical Priests	Messiah
Many priests	One
Standing	Sitting (finished)
Daily	One specific day
Repeated	Once for all
Many sacrifices	Only one
Temporary	Permanent
Covered sins	Took sins away

Danger of Willful Sin

Hebrews 10:26-31

- If they now apostasize from the faith and once and for all return to Judaism, there remains no more sacrifice for their sin.
  Cf. Heb 10:23-25 vs. 10:26-29
- It is a rejection of the work of the Trinity.
- God will judge His people. Deut 32:35-36
- It is a fearful thing to fall into the hands of the living God.

Hall of Faith

Hebrews 11

- Abel
- Enoch
- Noah
- Abraham
- Sarah
- Isaac
- Jacob
- Joseph
- Moses
- Joshua
- Rahab
- Gideon
- Barak
- Samson
- Jephthah
- David
- Samuel
- ...and the Prophets

Summary: 5 Warnings

- The Danger of Drifting 2:1-4
- The Danger of Disobedience 3:7-4:13
- Progress toward Maturity 5:11-6:20
  - Interim apostasy not an option
- The Danger of Willful Sin 10:26-31
- Warning against Indifference 12:25-29
  - In light of Better Blood in a Better Place

The Epistle of Jacob (James)

To the Twelve Tribes of the Dispersion

Conduct, not Creed; Behavior, not Belief; Deed, not Doctrine

- Endurance of Faith
  - Outward Trials & Inward Temptations 1:2-18
- Tests of the Genuineness of Faith
  - Response to the Word of God 1:19-27
  - Response to social distinctions 2:1-13
  - Production of good works 2:14-26
  - Exercise of self-control 3:1-18
  - Reaction to worldliness 4:1-5:12
  - Resort to prayer in all circumstances 5:12-18

1st Epistle of Peter

To the Elect Sojourners of the Dispersion

- The Status of the Believer 1 – 2:10
  - Foreknowledge of God
  - Unto Obedience of Faith
  - The Living Stone (to the Remnant)
    - Stone of Stumbling, Rock of Offense (to the non-Remnant) Psalm 118:22
- The Pilgrim Life 2:11-4:11
  - Citizens, Servants, Marriage
- The Fiery Trial 4:12 – 5:11
  - Rejoice; Commit; Be Vigilant
  - Farewell 5:12-14

2nd Epistle of Peter

- The Need to Grow 1
  - In Virtue, Knowledge, Self-Control, Patience, Godliness, Kindness, and Love
  - By "more sure Word of Prophecy"
- False Teachers 2
  - Will infect with slander and immorality
  - God delivers to/from judgment
    - Fallen Angels vs Noah and family Gen 6
    - Sodom & Gomorrah vs Lot and family Gen 19
- Promise for End-Times 3
  - Scoffers of 2nd Coming

1st Epistle of John

Truth versus Error

(Seven Contrasts)

1. The Light vs. The Darkness 1:5-2:11
2. The Father vs. The World 2:12-2:17
3. Christ vs. the Antichrist 2:18-2:28
4. Good Works vs. Evil Works 2:29-3:24
5. Holy Spirit vs. Error 4:1-4:6
6. Love vs. Pious Pretence 4:7-4:21
7. The God-Born vs. others 5:1-5:21

2nd Epistle of John

To the Elect Lady

- Practical: Walk in Love
  - The Divine insistence on love 4, 5
  - The Human expression of love 6
- Doctrinal: Watch Against Error
  - Warning against false teaching 7-9
  - Warning against false charity 10,11
  - Parting comments 12, 13

3rd Epistle of John

- Gaius: Service in Truth and Love 2-8
- Diotrephes: Evil by pride and strife 9-11
- Commendation of one
  - Demetrius 12
  - Parting words 13,14

The Epistle of Jude

Contend for the Faith

- *Why* to Contend: Apostates vv.3-16
  - Their subtle perversions
  - Their certain doom
  - Their impious ways
  - Their utter falsity
- *How* to Contend: Resources vv.17-23
  - Apostasy has been foretold
  - Build, Pray, Keep, Look…
  - Support those who contend

Learn the Bible in 24 Hours: Session 20

Hour 20: The Hebrew Epistles (Hebrews, James, Peter, John, Jude)

1) Why are these letters called the "Hebrew Epistles"?

2) Outline and summarize the key points in the Epistle to the Hebrews. How is it distinctive from the other epistles?

3) In what ways is the Epistle of James distinctive from Paul's? Are they compatible?

4) Summarize the two letters of Peter, and select two key ideas that were important to you.

5) To whom was 2 John written? Justify your answer.

6) What surprises are there in the Book of Jude?

7) Who was Melchizedek and why was he significant?

Group Discussion Questions: See *Small Group Leaders* section of this workbook.

Preparation for the Next Session:

A review of Eschatology: the study of "Last Things." Review 1 & 2 Thessalonians.

Learn the Bible
in 24 Hours
Hour Twenty-one
Eschatological Summary

The Return of Christ to Rule

- 1,845 references in the Old Testament
  - 17 books give prominence to the event
- 318 references in the New Testament
  - 216 chapters
  - 23 of 27 books give prominence to the event
- *For every prophecy of Christ's 1st Coming there are 8 of His 2nd Coming!*

The History of Amillennialism

- Origen: Allegorization of Scripture
- Augustine: Amillennialism
- Roman Catholic Eschatology
- Reformation failed to address…
  - Most Protestant Denominations are Amillennial and Post-Tribulational in their eschatological views

Divisions of Theology

• Bibliology	The Bible
• Theology Proper	Attributes of God
• Christology	Lord Jesus Christ
• Pneumatology	Holy Spirit
• Angelology	Angels, fallen and un-fallen
• Anthropology	Man
• Soteriology	Salvation
• Ecclesiology	The Church
• Eschatology	End-Times; Last Things
• Israelology	Israel as God's instrument

Israel and the Church

- Distinctions
  - Different Origins, Missions, Destinies
- "Replacement" views deny Israel its place in God's program
  - Makes God a Liar
  - Laid the basis for Christian Anti-Semitism
- The "70 Weeks" deal specifically with *Israel*
- Paul's dichotomy: Jews + Gentiles = Church
- Distinctives reappear after Revelation 4…

The *Harpazo*

Our Blessed Hope

For the Lord himself shall descend from heaven with a shout, with the voice of the archangel, and with the trump of God: and the dead in Christ shall rise first:

Then we which are alive and remain shall be caught up together with them in the clouds, to meet the Lord in the air: and so shall we ever be with the Lord.

1 Thessalonians 4:16, 17

The Order of Events

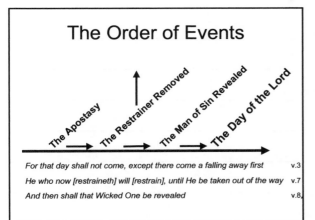

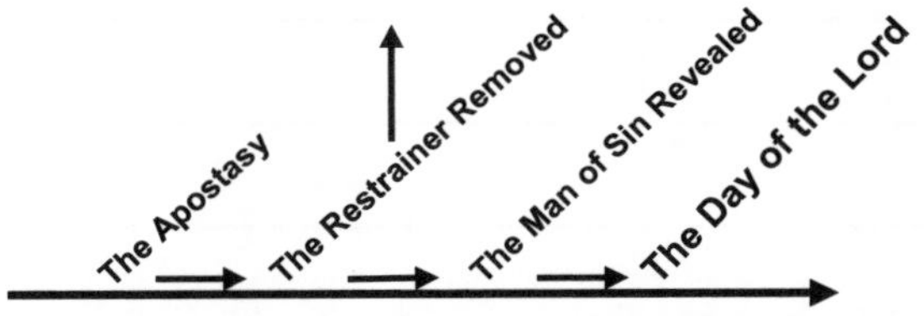

For that day shall not come, except there come a falling away first v.3

He who now [restraineth] will [restrain], until He be taken out of the way v.7

And then shall that Wicked One be revealed v.8

The Second Coming

Daniel 2:44-45	Acts 1:9-11
Daniel 7:9-14	Acts 3:19-21
Daniel 12:1-3	1 Thess 3:13
Zech 14:1-15	2 Thess 1:6-10
Matt 13:41	2 Thess 2:8
Matt 24:15-31	2 Peter 3:1-14
Matt 26:64	Jude 14-15
Mark 13:14-27	Rev 1:7
Mark 14:62	Rev 19:11-20
Luke 21:25-28	Rev 22:7, 12, 20

The "Rapture"

John 14:1-3	2 Thess 2:1, (3)
1 Cor 15:1-53	1 Tim 6:14
1 Thess 4:13-18	2 Tim 4:1
Rom 8:19	Titus 2:13
1 Cor 1:7-8	Heb 9:28
1 Cor 16:22	James 5:7-9
Phil 3:20-21	1 Peter 1:7, 13
Col 3:4	1 John 2:28-3:2
1 Thess 1:10	Jude 21
1 Thess 2:19	Rev 2:25
1 Thess 5:9	Rev 3:10
1 Thess 5:23	

Post-Tribulation Problems

- Denies NT teaching of Imminency
  - We are to expect at *any* time…
- Requires the Church during 70th Week
  - Israel and the Church mutually exclusive Dan 9:26
- Church experiences God's Wrath
  - Promised not to experience 1 Thess 5:9; Rev 3:10
- How can the Bride come *with* Him?

Alternative "Tribulation" Views

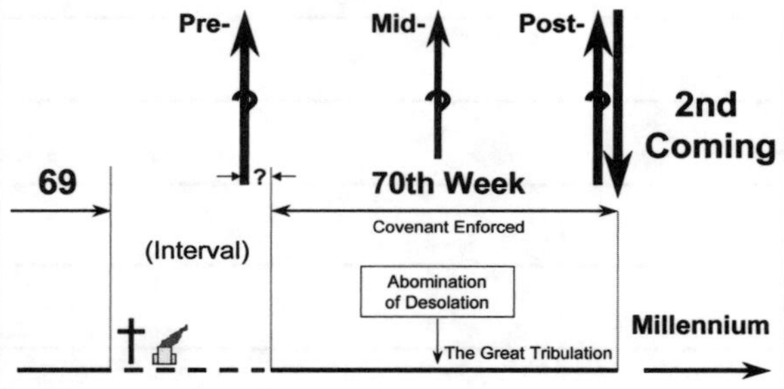

Rapture *precedes* the Tribulation?

- 70th Week is defined by covenant enforced by the Coming World Leader Daniel 9:27
- "Great Tribulation" = last 1/2 of 70th Week Matt 24:15, 21
- The Leader cannot be revealed until *after* the Rapture 2 Thess 2:6-9

Eschatology

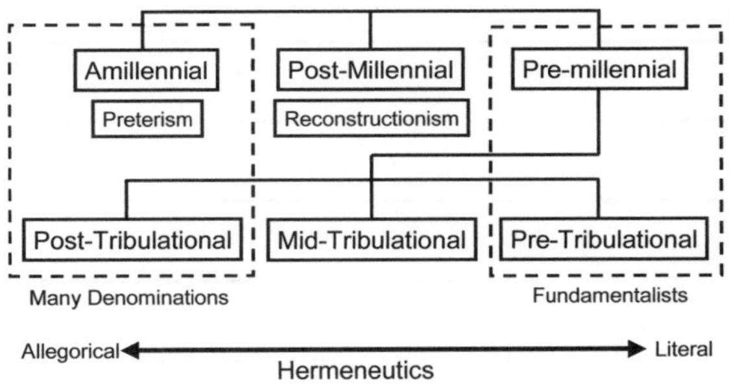

Pre-Tribulation Eschatology

- *Epistle of Barnabas,* (A.D. 100)
- Irenaeus, in *Against Heresies*
- Hippolytus, a disciple of Irenaeus (2nd Century)
- Justin Martyr, *Dialogue with Trypho*
- Ephraem, the Syrian (4th Century)

3 Groups Facing Flood of Noah

1. Those that *perished in* the Flood
2. Those *preserved through* the Flood
3. Those *removed prior* to the Flood

- Enoch Born: *Hag Shavout*
- Enoch Translated: *Hag Shavout*
- Church born: *Hag Shavout* *

* = Feast of Weeks, Harvest, Pentecost

"Rapture-itis"

- A uniquely American dementia
- Just because the Church will *not* go through The Great Tribulation,

  why should we escape
  what most of the Body of Christ
  in most of the world
  for most of the past 2,000 years
  has had to endure?

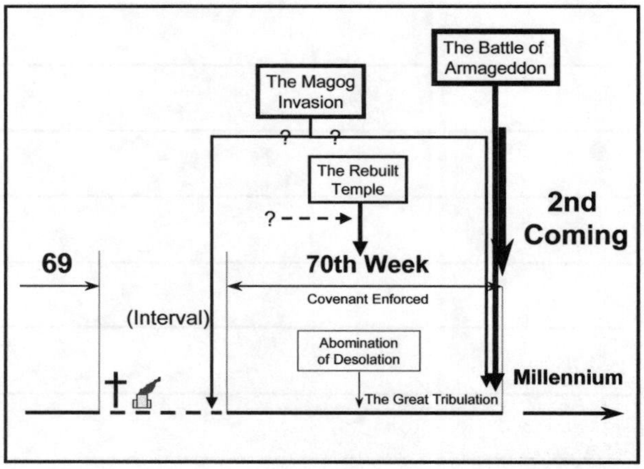

Strategic Trends

• Struggle for Jerusalem	Zech 12; Luke 21
• Magog Invasion	Eze 38, 39
• Rise of European Super State	Dan 2, 7
• Rise of China	Isa 49; Rev 19
• Toward Global Government	Dan 11, Rev 13
• Ecumenical Religion	Rev 13, 17, 18
• Global Pestilence	Rev 6:8
• Decline of United States	Hosea 4 – 14
• Weapons of Mass Destruction	Matt 24:22

Learn the Bible in 24 Hours: Session 21

Hour 21: Eschatological Summary (Thessalonians)

1) What is *eschatology*? How does it differ from "prophecy"?

2) Define the terms: Hermeneutics, Millennium, Amillennial, Premillennial, "Pre-Trib," "Post-Trib," and "Mid-Trib."

3) What is the origin of the "Amillennial" viewpoint and in what way does it seem to denigrate God's character? In what way was this view a *failure* of the Reformation?

4) In what ways is the origin and destiny of "Israel" distinct from that of the "church"? How are they similar?

5) What is the "Great Tribulation" and what is its purpose?

6) In what ways is the "*harpazo*" distinct from the Second Coming? What are the prerequisite conditions for each?

7) What is the "Doctrine of Imminence"?

8) Sketch a time line of the principal events of the "End Times."

Group Discussion Questions: See *Small Group Leaders* section of this workbook.

Preparation for the Next Session:

Read Chapters 1 through 3 of the Book of Revelation.

Learn the Bible
in 24 Hours

Hour Twenty-two

Revelation 1 - 3

"He Shall Glorify Me" John 16:14

- Old Testament
  - Christ in Prophecy "Behold, He Comes!"
- Gospels
  - Christ in History "Behold, He Dies!"
- Acts
  - Christ in the Church "Behold, He Lives!"
- Epistles
  - Christ in Experience "Behold, He Saves!"
- Apocalypse
  - Christ in coming Glory "Behold, He Reigns!"

Vision in Chapter 1
Seven Features

1) Hair; head	Dan 7:9
2) Eyes, Flame of fire	Heb 1:13; 4:13; 1 Cor 3:13; Mal 3:2, etc
3) Feet, Brass	symbol of walk judgment [cf. Brazen serpent Nu 21]
4) Voice, many waters	Ez 1:24; 43:2; Dan 10:6
5) Right Hand	7 stars, lampstands: in the midst; in His hand
6) Mouth: two-edged sword	Heb 4:12; Eph 6:17; Isa 49:2
Judges unbeliever	John 12:48
Earth smitten	Isa 11:4
Antichrist consumed	2 Thess 2:8
7) Countenance, Sun	Matt 17

The Divine Outline

Revelation 1:19

Write the things which ***thou hast seen,***

The Vision of Christ, Chapter 1

and the things which ***are,***

The Seven Churches, Chapters 2 & 3

and the things which ***shall be hereafter;***

That which follows <u>*after*</u> the Churches;

Chapters 4-22

The Seven Churches

"The Things that are"

- Why *these* seven?

  He that hath an ear let him hear what the Spirit says to the churches."

- Levels of Application:

  Local

  Admonitory

  Homiletic (Personal)

  Prophetic

Seven Design Elements

In Each of the Letters to Seven Churches

1. Name of the Church
2. Title of Christ Chosen
3. Commendation
4. Concern
5. Exhortation
6. Promise to the Overcomer
7. "He that hath an ear, hear what the Spirit says to the churches."

Letter to Ephesus

"Darling"

Unto the angel of the church of Ephesus write;

Title:

These things saith he that holdeth the seven stars in his right hand, who walketh in the midst of the seven golden lampstands;

Commendation:

I know thy works, and thy labour, and thy patience, and how thou canst not bear them which are evil: and thou hast tried them which say they are apostles, and are not, and hast found them liars:

And hast borne, and hast patience, and for my name's sake hast laboured, and hast not fainted.

Revelation 2:1-3

Letter to Smyrna

"Myrrh"

And unto the angel of the church in Smyrna write;

Title:

These things saith the first and the last, which was dead, and is alive;

Commendation:

I know thy works, and tribulation, and poverty, (but thou art rich) and I know the blasphemy of them which say they are Jews, and are not, but are the synagogue of Satan.

Revelation 2:8, 9

Letter to Pergamos

"Mixed Marriage"

And to the angel of the church in Pergamos write;

Title:

These things saith he which hath the sharp sword with two edges;

Commendation:

I know thy works, and where thou dwellest, even where Satan's seat is: and thou holdest fast my name, and hast not denied my faith, even in those days wherein Antipas was my faithful martyr, who was slain among you, where Satan dwelleth.

Revelation 2:12-13

Letter to Thyatira

"Semiramis"

And unto the angel of the church in Thyatira write;

Title:

These things saith the Son of God, who hath his eyes like unto a flame of fire, and his feet are like fine brass;

Commendation:

I know thy works, and charity, and service, and faith, and thy patience, and thy works; and the last to be more than the first.

Revelation 2:18, 19

Letter to Sardis

"Remnant"

And unto the angel of the church in Sardis write;

Title:

These things saith he that hath the seven Spirits of God, and the seven stars;

Concern:

I know thy works, that thou hast a name that thou livest, and art dead.

Exhortation:

Be watchful, and strengthen the things which remain, that are ready to die: for I have not found thy works perfect before God.

Revelation 3:1, 2

Letter to Philadelphia

"Brotherly Love"

And to the angel of the church in Philadelphia write;

Title:

These things saith he that is holy, he that is true, he that hath the key of David, he that openeth, and no man shutteth; and shutteth, and no man openeth;

Commendation:

I know thy works: behold, I have set before thee an open door, and no man can shut it: for thou hast a little strength, and hast kept my word, and hast not denied my name. Revelation 3:7, 8

Letter to Laodicea

"Rule of the People"

And unto the angel of the church of the Laodiceans write;

Title:

These things saith the Amen, the faithful and true witness, the beginning of the creation of God;

Concerns:

I know thy works, that thou art neither cold nor hot: I would thou wert cold or hot.

So then because thou art lukewarm, and neither cold nor hot, I will spue thee out of my mouth.

Revelation 3:14-16

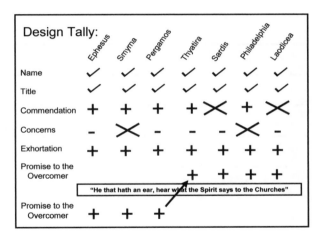

Design Tally:

	Ephesus	Smyrna	Pergamos	Thyatira	Sardis	Philadelphia	Laodicea
Name	✓	✓	✓	✓	✓	✓	✓
Title	✓	✓	✓	✓	✓	✓	✓
Commendation	+	+	+	+	X	+	X
Concerns	-	X	-	-	-	X	-
Exhortation	+	+	+	+	+	+	+
Promise to the Overcomer				+	+	+	+

"He that hath an ear, hear what the Spirit says to the Churches"

	Ephesus	Smyrna	Pergamos	Thyatira	Sardis	Philadelphia	Laodicea
Promise to the Overcomer	+	+	+				

Prophetic Profile?

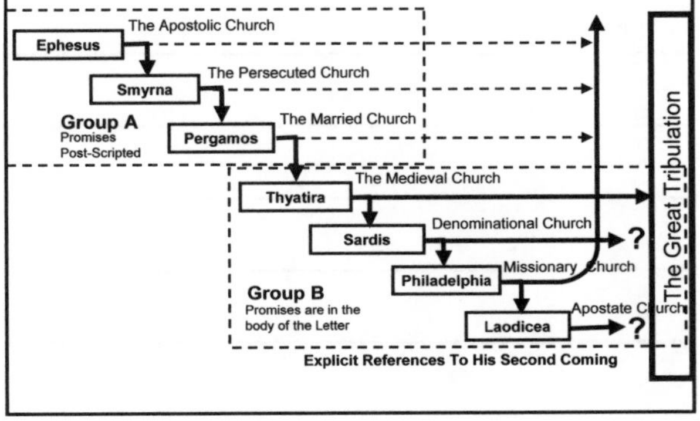

The Seven Kingdom Parables

Rev. 2 & 3	Matthew 13
• Ephesus	• The Sower and 4 Soils
• Smyrna	• The Tares and the Wheat
• Pergamos	• The Mustard Seed
• Thyatira	• The Woman & the Leaven
• Sardis	• The Treasure in the Field
• Philadelphia	• The Pearl of Great Price
• Laodicea	• The Dragnet

Seven Churches

Jesus:	Paul:
• Ephesus	• Ephesus
• Smyrna	• Philippians
• Pergamos	• Corinthians
• Thyatira	• Galatians
• Sardis	• Romans
• Philadelphia	• Thessalonians
• Laodicea	• Colossians

The Apocalypse

- Catastrophic End-crisis of present age
- Spectacular reappearance of the King of Kings in His global empire
- Internment of Satan in the *Abousso*
- Millennial earth-reign of Christ
- Final insurrection and the abolition of sin
- New Heaven and New Earth

Learn the Bible in 24 Hours: Session 22

Hour 22: The Once and Future Church (Revelation 1-3)

1) What promises have been given to the reader of this particular book?

2) Why does this book seem inaccessible to the average Bible reader? How many Old Testament allusions are contained in its 404 verses?

3) What is the outline of the book given in Chapter 1?

4) What seven elements make up the design inherent in the letters to the seven churches? Which letters have significant *omissions*? Compile a chart including all seven (on a separate piece of paper).

5) What are the four distinctive levels of interpretation of the seven letters?

6) Summarize the key points and principal issues in each of the letters.

7) What are the distinctives that distinguish between the first three and the final four letters? What are the implications?

8) Summarize the reasons why some believe the seven letters form an anticipatory profile of the history of the "church."

Group Discussion Questions: See *Small Group Leaders* section of this workbook.

Preparation for the Next Session:

Read Revelation 4 through 22.

Learn the Bible

in 24 Hours

Hour Twenty-three

Revelation 4 - 22

The Throne Room of Universe

Revelation 4

- Throne of God 2, 3
- 24 Elders 4
  - Kings and Priests: the Redeemed
- 7 Lamps burning 5
- Sea of Glass 6
  - Elders *standing* on it
- 4 Living Creatures (Cherubim) 6-8
  - 4 faces: Lion, Calf, Man, Eagle

The Kinsman-Redeemer

And one of the elders saith unto me,
"Weep not: behold, ***the Lion of the tribe of Judah, the Root of David****, hath prevailed to open the book, and to loose the seven seals thereof."*

And I beheld, and, lo, in the midst of the throne and of the four living creatures, and in the midst of the elders, stood ***the Lamb as it had been slain****, having seven horns and seven eyes, which are the seven Spirits of God sent forth into all the earth.*

Revelation 5:5-6

The Sealing of the 144,000

Revelation 7

Judah	12,000	Simeon	12,000
Reuben	12,000	Levi	12,000
Gad	12,000	Issachar	12,000
Asher	12,000	Zebulun	12,000
Naphtali	12,000	Joseph	12,000
Manasseh	12,000	Benjamin	12,000

Where is the Tribe of Dan?
Where is the Tribe of Ephraim?

The Little Book

Revelation 10

- Parenthetical: Chapters 10-14
  - 7th Trumpet ushers in the Bowls of Wrath
- Mighty Angel with the "Little Book"
  - Book is now unsealed: digest it
  - Written "within and on the backside"
  - "Thou must prophesy again…"
- The Seven Thunders utter their voices
  - John was about to write, but forbidden to

The Two Witnesses

Revelation 11

- Temple measured
  - Outer Court to Gentiles: 42 months
- Two Witnesses empowered: 1260 days
  - Call down fire from heaven] Elijah?
  - Shut heaven, no rain
  - Turn water into blood] Moses?
  - Smite earth with plagues
- Beast from the Abousso kills them
  - Earth-dwellers celebrate
  - Resurrected after 3 ½ days

The Woman and Man-Child
Revelation 12

• Woman	Israel
– with sun, moon, 12 stars	
– With child	
• Red Dragon	Serpent, Devil, Satan
– 7 heads, 10 horns, 7 crowns	
– To devour Man-child when born	
• Man-Child	Kinsman-Redeemer
– To rule all nations with rod of iron	
– Caught up to God and His throne	
– Woman flees into wilderness,	1260 days
• Michael and His Angels	
– Fights Dragon and his angels	
• Dragon cast to earth	
– Persecutes the Woman	3 ½ years

The Two Beasts
Revelation 13

- Beast out of the Sea
  - 7 Heads, 10 Horns
  - Heads with the name of blasphemy
  - One of heads: deadly wound healed
  - Powered by the Dragon for 42 months
  - Overcomes the Saints
  - Earth-Dwellers worship
    - All those not written in the Book of Life

The Two Beasts
Revelation 13

- Beast out of the Earth ("False Prophet")
  - Two horns like Lamb
  - Speaks as the Dragon
  - Causes Earth to worship the 1st Beast
  - Deceives the Earth with miracles
  - Forces worship of an image of 1st Beast
    - All receive mark in right hands or foreheads
    - No man may buy or sell without the name or number of the 1st Beast: 666

The Seven Bowls of Wrath

Chapters 15 & 16

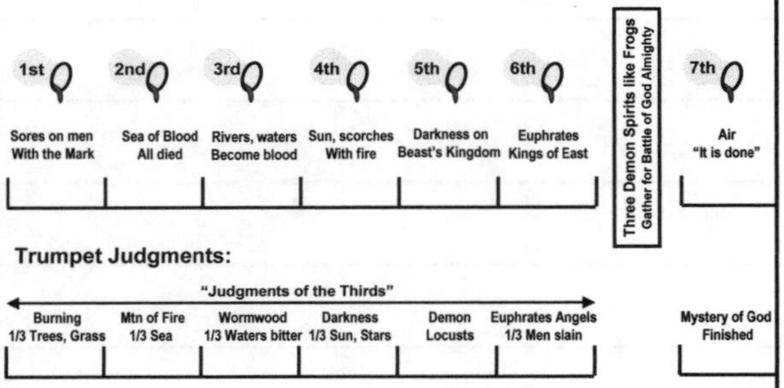

The Armageddon Scenario

Daniel 11

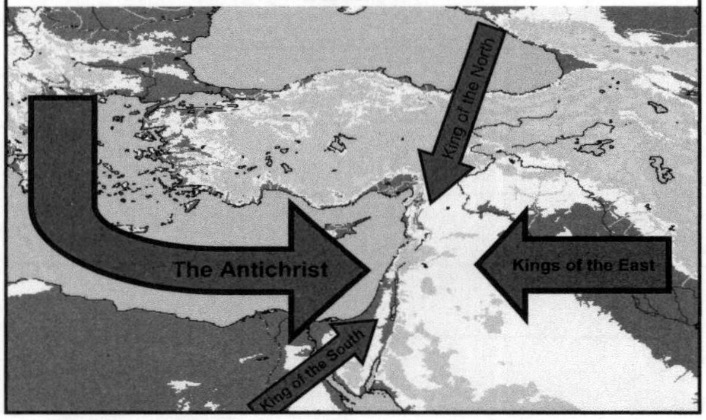

Mystery Babylon

Revelation 17 & 18

- The Great Whore 17
  - Rides the Beast with 7 heads, 10 horns
  - Mother of Harlots and Abominations
  - Drunk with the blood of the saints
- Babylon the Great (City) 18
  - Kings
  - Merchants
  - Those that trade by sea

The "Fifth Horseman"

Revelation 19

*11 And I saw heaven opened, and behold a **white** horse; and he that sat upon him was called **Faithful and True**, and in righteousness he doth judge and make war.*

12 His eyes were as a flame of fire, and on his head were many crowns; and he had a name written, that no man knew, but he himself.

*13 And he was clothed with a vesture dipped in blood: and his name is called **The Word of God**.*

The "Fifth Horseman"

Revelation 19

14 And the armies which were in heaven followed him upon white horses, clothed in fine linen, white and clean.

15 And out of his mouth goeth a sharp sword, that with it he should smite the nations: and he shall rule them with a rod of iron: and he treadeth the winepress of the fierceness and wrath of Almighty God.

16 And he hath on his vesture and on his thigh a name written, KING OF KINGS, AND LORD OF LORDS.

The Millennium

Revelation 20

- Promised to David,
  - 2 Sam 7:12-17; 23:5;
  - Under oath: Ps 89:34-37;
- Predicted in the Psalms and the Prophets:
  - Ps 2; 45; 110; Isa 2:1-5; 4:1-6; 11:1-9; 12:1-6; 30:18-26; 35:1-10; 60, 61:3-62; 66; Jer 23:3-8; 32:37-44; Eze 40-48; Dan 2:44-45; 7:13-14; 12:2-3; Mic 4:1-8; Zech 12:10-14:21.
- Promised to Mary,
  - Luke 1:32; Micah 5:2; Isa 9:6, 7; Dan 2:44; reaffirmed to apostles: Luke 22:29-30.
- Lord's Prayer: "Thy Kingdom come";
  - Matt 6:10, 13; Acts 1:6; Ps 45, 46, 47, 48
- Rule: Psalm 2; 110;
  - "Rod of Iron" Rev 12:5; 19:15;
  - "Every knee will bow," Phil 2:6-11

The Millennium
Revelation 20

- Creation changed:
  - Physical changes — Zech 4:9,10; Isa 35:1-10
  - Curse lifted — Isa 11:6-9
  - Creation redeemed — Gen 3 → Rom 8:20-22
  - Earth full of knowledge of the Lord — Isa 11:9; Hab 2:14
- Yet, not eternity: — Isa 65
  - Death, sin — Isa 65:20
  - Each to have land — Micah 4:15
  - Fruitful — Amos 9:13

The New Jerusalem

- 12 Gates, named with the 12 Tribes
- 12 Foundations, named with 12 apostles
- Cubical?
  - 12,000 furlongs *in each of 3 dimensions* (1500 miles?)
- No Temple: dwelling with God
- No night: Lamb is the light thereof
- Tree of Life, etc.

Epilog
Revelation 22

16 I Jesus have sent mine angel to testify unto you these things in the churches. I am the root and the offspring of David, and the bright and morning star.

17 And the Spirit and the bride say, Come. And let him that heareth say, Come. And let him that is athirst come. And whosoever will, let him take the water of life freely.

20 …Surely I come quickly. Amen. Even so, come, Lord Jesus.

Learn the Bible in 24 Hours: Session 23

Hour 23: The Seals, Trumpets, Bowls, and Triumph (Revelation 4 - 22)

1) Why do some scholars believe that the *harpazo* is implied in the opening of Chapter 4?

2) Who are the 24 Elders? Why?

3) Who are the Woman and the Man-Child in Chapter 12? How do we know?

4) Contrast the Harlot and the Beast she rides.

5) What is the basis for expecting a literal "Millennium"? How does it differ from the eternal state that follows?

Group Discussion Questions: See *Small Group Leaders* section of this workbook.

Preparation for the Next Session:

Review your previous notes for the final summary. How has this study benefited *you*?

Whence Next?

After the conclusion next week, it would be well to embark on a verse-by-verse expositional study, book-by-book—in any appealing order—either individually or among a small group. And watch what *He* does… This, indeed, is the greatest adventure conceivable!

Learn the Bible
in 24 Hours
Hour Twenty-four

Conclusion

Old Testament

Torah - 5
- Genesis
- Exodus
- Leviticus
- Numbers
- Deuteronomy

Historical - 12
- Joshua
- Judges
- Ruth
- 1 Samuel
- 2 Samuel
- 1 Kings
- 2 Kings
- 1 Chronicles
- 2 Chronicles
- Ezra
- Nehemiah
- Esther

Poetical Books - 5
- Job
- Psalms
- Proverbs
- Ecclesiastes
- Song of Songs

Major Prophets - 5
- Isaiah
- Jeremiah
  - Lamentations
- Ezekiel
- Daniel

Minor Prophets - 12
- Hosea
- Joel
- Amos
- Obadiah
- Jonah
- Micah
- Nahum
- Habakkuk
- Zephaniah
- Haggai
- Zechariah
- Malachi

The Torah

Genesis	The Book of Beginnings
Exodus	The Birth of the Nation
Leviticus	The Law of the Nation
Numbers	The Wilderness Wanderings
Deuteronomy	The Laws Reviewed

The Scarlet Thread

- The "Seed of the Woman" Genesis 3:15
  - The Race
- Abraham Genesis 22:18
  - The Nation
- Jacob Genesis 49:10
  - The Tribe
- David 2 Samuel 7:11-16
  - The Family

The Historical Books

Joshua	The Conquest of Canaan
Judges	The First 300 Years
Ruth	The Kinsman-Redeemer
1 Samuel	The Birth of the Kingdom
2 Samuel	Reign of David
1 Kings	The Kingdom Divided
2 Kings	History of the Divided Kingdom
1 Chronicles	Reign of David
2 Chronicles	History of the Southern Kingdom

Historical Books (Post-Exile)

Ezra	Return from Captivity
Nehemiah	Rebuilding Jerusalem
Esther	Escape from Extermination

Poetical Books

Job	Why do the innocent suffer?
Psalms	The Hymn Book of Israel
Proverbs	Wisdom of Solomon
Ecclesiastes	All is Vanity
Song of Songs	Wedded Love

Major Prophets

Isaiah	The Messianic Prophet
Jeremiah	The Desolation of Jerusalem
Lamentations	Dirge over Jerusalem
Ezekiel	The Coming Restoration
Daniel	The Times of the Gentiles

"Minor" Prophets

Hosea	Apostasy of the Northern Kingdom
Joel	The Day of the Lord
Amos	Ultimate Rule of David
Obadiah	Destruction of Edom
Jonah	A Warning to Nineveh
Micah	A Birth in Bethlehem
Nahum	Destruction of Nineveh
Habakkuk	"The Just Shall Live By Faith"
Zephaniah	The Coming of a "Pure Language"
Haggai	Rebuilding the Temple
Zechariah	The Second Coming
Malachi	Final Message to a Disobedient People

Old Testament Summary

- Old Testament leaves open:
  - Unexplained ceremonies (sacrificial rituals)
  - Unachieved purposes (covenants)
  - Unappeased longings (poetical books)
  - Unfulfilled prophecies (incomplete…)

"Search the scriptures; for in them ye think ye have eternal life: and they are they which testify of me." John 5:39

New Testament

Historical Books - 5	Paul's Epistles - 13	Prophetic - 1
Matthew	Romans	Revelation
Mark	1, 2 Corinthians	
Luke	Galatians	
John	Ephesians	
	Philippians	
Acts	Colossians	
	1, 2 Thessalonians	
	1, 2 Timothy	
	Titus	
	Philemon	
	Hebrew Epistles - 8	
	Hebrews	
	James	
	1, 2 Peter	
	1, 2, 3, John	
	Jude	

The Design of the Gospels

	Matthew	Mark	Luke	John
Presents as:	Messiah	Servant	Son of Man	Son of God
Genealogy:	Abraham (Legal)	--	Adam (Blood line)	Eternal (Preexistence)
What Jesus	Said	Did	Felt	Was
To the:	Jew	Roman	Greek	Church
1st Miracle:	Leper cleansed (Jew = sin)	Demon expelled	Demon expelled	Water to Wine
Ends with	Resurrection	Ascension	Promise of Spirit: Acts	Promise of Return: Revelation
Camp Side:	East	West	South	North
Ensign:	Judah	Ephraim	Reuben	Dan
Face:	**Lion**	**Ox**	**Man**	**Eagle**
Style:	Groupings	Snapshots	Narrative	Mystical

Acts (of the Holy Spirit)

• Ascension	1
• Pentecost – Birth of the Church	2
• Outrage against Stephen	7
• Philip & Ethiopian Treasurer	8
• Call of Paul	9
• Peter's Vision at Cornelius'	10
• Mission to Gentiles	11-14
• Council at Jerusalem	15

Acts (Continued)

• 1st Missionary Journey	13, 14
• 2nd Missionary Journey	15
– Athens, Mars Hill	17
• 3rd Missionary Journey	18
• Outcry against Paul	22
– Before Sanhedrin	23
– Before Governor Felix	24
– Before Governor Festus	25
– Before King Agrippa	26
• Paul goes to Rome	27-28

Pauline Epistles

Romans	Definitive Doctrines
1, 2 Corinthians	Order in the Church
Galatians	Law vs. Grace
Ephesians	The Mystery of the Church
Philippians	Resources in Suffering
Colossians	Christ Pre-eminent
1, 2 Thessalonians	The Second Coming
1, 2 Timothy	Pastoral Advice
Titus	Pastoral Advice
Philemon	Intercessionary Example

Hebrew Christian Epistles

Hebrews	The New Covenant
James	Faith Demonstrated
1 Peter	Persecuted Church
2 Peter	Coming Apostasy
1 John	Love
2 John	False Teachers
3 John	Preparation of Helpers
Jude	Apostasy

Eschatology

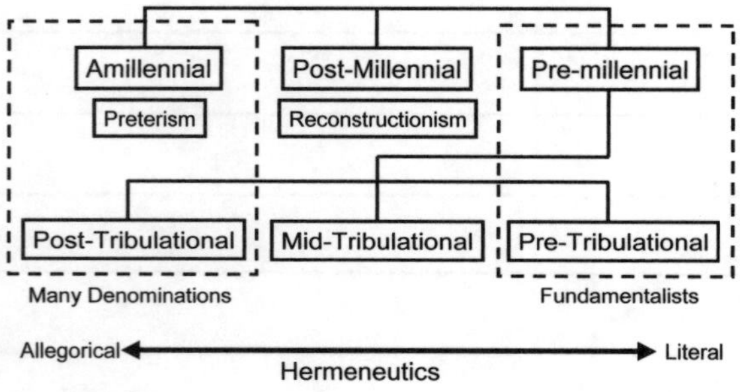

The Ultimate Issue

- We are in possession of a message of extraterrestrial origin.
- It portrays us as objects of an unseen warfare.
- Our eternal destiny depends upon our relationship with the ultimate victor in this cosmic conflict.
- Where do *you* stand with respect to *Him*?

Learn the Bible in 24 Hours: Session 24

Hour 24: Conclusion

1) Compile a list of concepts that were introduced in Genesis and concluded in Revelation.

2) Summarize the key concept in each of the five books of the *Torah*.

3) Summarize the key aspect of each of the books of the New Testament.

4) What makes the Bible distinctive over all other documents and sources of information? Why can (must) we rely on it for our eternal destiny?

5) How has this study impacted you *personally*?

Group Discussion Questions: See *Small Group Leaders* section of this workbook.

Congratulations! You're done!

Discussion Questions for Small Group Leaders

For Every Session:

1) What in this session impacted you the most regarding the integrity of the Bible as a whole?
2) What lessons in this session caused you to take the Bible more seriously?
3) How did this session impact you *personally*?

Session 1—Hour 1: Introduction

1) Discuss three discoveries of 20th century science that vindicate the Biblical perspective of reality.
2) Name two mathematical concepts that elude empirical verification. What inferences may we draw from this?
3) Name three theories of the skeptics, and three factors that refute them.

Session 2—Hour 2: The Fall of Man (Genesis 1 - 3)

1) Explain the "Gap Theory" and explore the arguments pro and con.
2) How have the "information sciences" destroyed the Darwinian theory of biogenesis?

Session 3—Hour 3: The Pre-History Period (Genesis 4 - 11)

1) What are the implications of the message hidden in Genesis 5?
2) Discuss at least four reasons the common "line of Seth" theory of Genesis 6 is not Scriptural.
3) What lessons do we learn from Noah's Ark and the flood?

Session 4—Hour 4: The Patriarchs (Genesis 12 - 50)

1) How is the Abrahamic Covenant being challenged today? By whom?
2) Explore the numerous details that were prophetic in Abraham's offering of Isaac.
3) Compare the *prophetic* parallels of Genesis 22 and 24.

Session 5—Hour 5: The Birth of the Nation (Exodus - Deuteronomy)

1) Should a Christian celebrate the Feasts of Israel?
2) Is the Sabbath on Saturday or Sunday? What is the relevance of the Sabbath to the Christian?
3) What is the significance of Leviticus to a New Testament believer?
4) Why are there *Nephilim* referred to in Numbers 13:33?

Session 6—Hour 6: In the Land (Joshua, Judges, Ruth)

1) Did the sun really "stand still" for Joshua?
2) What are the lessons of the Book of Judges for us *today*?
3) List the prophetic implications of the details in the Book of Ruth. Why is it associated with the Feast of Weeks?

Session 7—Hour 7: The Monarchy (Samuel, Kings, Chronicles)

1) Contrast the careers of Saul, David and Solomon.
2) Why was the Southern Kingdom allowed to return after their exile, while the Northern Kingdom was obliterated?
3) In what way(s) is the principle that God declares in 2 Chronicles 7:14 applicable to America?
4) Why are the "Lost Ten Tribes" regarded as an unbiblical myth?

Session 8—Hour 8: The Poetical Books

1) Why weren't Job's sons and daughters "doubled" in Chapter 42?
2) Which Psalms have had a specific impact on *your* life?
3) In what way is Ecclesiastes more bravely honest than pessimistic?
4) Is Song of Songs a love-making guide, a literal historical episode, or a royal marriage allegory?

Session 9—Hour 9: The Book of Daniel

1) Why is Daniel 9:25 considered to be one of the most profound proofs of Jesus as the Messiah?
2) What is the principal insights of Chapter 10?
3) Is the rise of a European Superstate a prelude to the destinies portrayed in Daniel 2 & 7?
4) Does the current rebuilding of the city of Babylon have Biblical significance? Why?

Session 10—Hour 10: Post-Exile History

1) Why did the Southern Kingdom survive when the Northern Kingdom did not?
2) What were the *leadership* lessons of Nehemiah?
3) What are the *personal* lessons from the Book of Esther? Why are there hidden acrostics and other codes behind the text?

Session 11—Hour 11: The Major Prophets (Isaiah, Jeremiah, Ezekiel)

1) Why a virgin birth? (Isaiah 7:14)
2) In what sense is Isaiah 53 *yet* to be fulfilled?
3) Is the Magog Invasion of Ezekiel 38 and 39 imminent? Is it part of the Armageddon scenario, or is it a prelude? Why do many scholars believe it will occur *after* the Rapture? How does it compare to (another?) "God and Magog" event *after* the Millennium?

Session 12—Hour 12: The Minor Prophets

1) Is there a parallel between the Northern Kingdom under Jeroboam II and America today?
2) How is the Book of Jonah relevant to America today? Is there a life cycle of nations? Is America overdue for judgment? How can a national life be extended?
3) When does the Old Testament end? (It's not with Malachi.)

Session 13—Hour 13: How Sure Can We Be?

1) Are there any other "facts" that we know with as much certainty?
2) What other prophecies, in themselves, constitute extraordinary validations of the Biblical text?
3) Are there any other "sources" that can offer the same scrutiny or track record?
4) Discuss prophetic expectations on our near horizon.

Session 14—Hour 14: The New Testament (How We Got Our Bible)

1) How do we know that the Old Testament documents are reliable?
2) How do we know that the New Testament documents are reliable?
3) What are the advantages of the King James Version? What are the disadvantages?
4) Which version of the Bible is "best"? For whom, and under what conditions?

Session 15—Hour 15: The Gospels (Matthew, Mark, Luke, John)

1) Which of the Gospels is the most "Jewish"? The most "Gentile"? The most "mystical"?
2) Which of the Gospels has had the most impact on *your* life?
3) Do the four Gospels demonstrate any symbolic, or metaphorical relationships with the four ensigns mustering the Camp of Israel around the Tabernacle?

Session 16—Hour 16: The Final Week

1) Why was Christ crucified?
2) Was the Crucifixion a tragedy or an achievement? Why?
3) How do we know that Jesus was resurrected from the dead?
4) What do we know about Jesus' resurrection body? How is 1 John 3:2 a scientific statement?
5) Why did they have difficulty recognizing Him?

Session 17—Hour 17: The Book of Acts

1) In what ways is the Book of Acts a) A gateway to the Epistles? b) A prelude to the Book of Revelation?
2) Does a Christian need to "remember the Sabbath"? In what ways does the Council of Jerusalem impact our understanding of this issue?

Session 18—Hour 18: The Book of Romans

1) In what way is the Book of Romans the most comprehensive book in the New Testament?
2) In what way has it impacted the history of the world?
3) How does a Christian keep from sin?
4) How does the Book of Romans impact our *prophetic* perspective?

Session 19—Hour 19: Paul's Church and Pastoral Epistles

1) Where did Paul get his authority? Why are his letters in our Bible? What is their relevance today?
2) Is the Gospel preached in most churches? If not, why not?
3) Are the Pastoral Epistles for the average Christian? (Can one be a Christian and *not* be in the full-time ministry?)
4) How do we keep from being deceived?

Session 20—Hour 20: The Hebrew Epistles

1) Are we saved by faith or by works? Do Paul and James disagree on this?
2) Can you be lost once you have been saved?

Session 21—Hour 21: Eschatological Review

1) In what way(s) does your view of eschatology derive from your *hermeneutics*?
2) Will Jesus Christ rule the Planet Earth literally from the Throne of David in Israel?
3) Will the Church go through the "Great Tribulation"? Justify your view.
4) What are the practical hazards inherent in the "pre-tribulational" view?

Session 22—Hour 22: Revelation 1-3

1) Do the seven letters profile the history of the church?
2) Where are we today?
3) What are the *personal* implications and lessons of the letters?

Session 23—Hour 23: Revelation 4-22

1) Has this book been a blessing to *you*? How?
2) Why is the "Jewishness" of the text (after Chapter 4) significant?
3) How does the Seventy Weeks prophecy (of Daniel 9) impact our understanding of this book?
4) Who are the Two Witnesses?

Session 24—Hour 24: Conclusion

1) What is the most important priority in our lives that emerges from this study?
2) Can anyone understand the Scriptures without the Holy Spirit's involvement? How do you enlist His involvement?
3) *Use this discussion period to offer your personal testimony of your relationship with Jesus Christ.*

Topics for Research Papers

Session 1:

1) Make a list of the books of the Bible, and include a descriptive phrase that summarizes it.
2) Summarize the major discoveries of 20th century science and their implications on a Biblical view of reality.
3) Make a list of the most common objections to taking the Bible seriously and suggest rebuttals to each.
4) Contrast and compare two Bible Handbooks for their perspectives of the Bible as a whole.

Session 2:

1) Compile a list of authentications of Genesis by Jesus Christ.
2) Organize a detailed sketch of an "Entropy Map" of the early chapters of Genesis, and include annotations of the recent advances in science that impact our understanding of each progressive change in the entropy of the universe.
3) Explore contemporary perspectives of the *digital* limitations on our perception of reality—from the non-locality of subatomic particles to the quantized nature of the red shift of distant galaxies.
4) Contrast and compare two expositional commentaries on the Book of Genesis.

Session 3:

1) What major promises did God give to Abraham? To Israel? To David? Compare and contrast.
2) From Genesis 11, where would we expect to find Mt. Ararat?
3) Build a scale model (HO gauge or other) of Noah's Ark, including modern elements to convey comparable scales, etc.
4) Compare and contrast two expositional commentaries in their treatment of the first 11 chapters of Genesis.

Session 4:

1) Make a list of, and explain, the features that are prophetically relevant in Abraham's offering of Isaac.
2) Compare the 20 times that the "12 Tribes" are listed in the Bible, and explain why there are different tribes omitted. Summarize the strange treatment of the Tribe of Dan.
3) Compile a summary of the various prophecies of each of the tribes: Gen 49, Deut 33, et al.
4) Compile a list of, and explain, the myths being widely promoted regarding the plight of the Palestinians in Israel today.

Session 5:

1) Make a detailed model of the Tabernacle. Compile a list of details which can be associated *prophetically* with Jesus Christ.
2) Explore the *prophetic* role of the each of the seven feasts of Israel.
3) Beginning with the *Sh'ma* (Deut 6), compile references to the Trinity in the Old Testament.
4) If Moses had *not* disobeyed God in the second occasion of water being provided out of the rock, how might the *two* occasions been prophetic of 1 Corinthians 10:4? Does this explain the severity of the consequences Moses encountered? Explain.

Session 6:

1) Detail the Book of Joshua as a foreshadowing of the Book of Revelation.
2) Contrast Joshua as a primer on "victorious Christian living" with the Epistle to the Ephesians.
3) Who were the *Rephaim* and how do they compare with the *Nephilim*? Why was Joshua instructed to wipe out every man, women, and children of certain tribes?
4) Review the Book of Judges *geographically* and compare with the disputed territories *today.*

Session 7:

1) Make a comprehensive time profile of the kings in both the Northern and Southern Kingdoms, and the prophets that ministered during their reigns.
2) Study the reasons that the myth of the "Lost Ten Tribes" is not Biblical.
3) Review a Biblically sound biography of David.
4) Build a detailed model of the Temple of Solomon.

Session 8:

1) Compile a list of the science topics alluded to in the Book of Job.
2) Summarize the Messianic prophecies found in the Psalms.
3) Contrast the various perspectives of the Song of Songs, from allegories to royal marriage hymn.

Session 9:

1) Contrast the Fall of Babylon (Daniel 5) with the Doom of Babylon (prophesied in Isaiah 13, 14 and Jeremiah 50, 51). How is this relevant *today*?
2) Trace the history of the European Union and its relevance to the prophecies in Daniel 2 & 7.

Session 10:

1) Detail how the *genealogy* of Mordecai and Haman impact the interwoven dramas in the Book of Esther.
2) Explore the use of acrostics and other codes in the Biblical text. Give examples.

Session 11:

1) Compile a list of rebuttals to the "Deutero-Isaiah" conjectures.
2) What are the implications of the Ethiopian treasurer (Acts 8) reading Isaiah 52 & 53? Why is he in Jerusalem? Why is he heading home confused? What might this have to do with the Ark of the Covenant?
3) Compare Jesus' reading of Isaiah 61:1-2 in Luke 4 and note the implications when He stopped at a comma…

Session 12:

1) Write a biography on John the Baptist and his ministry.
2) Research the following questions: How was the Old Testament compiled? How do the Septuagint and Masoretic manuscripts fit in? What are their relative strengths and weaknesses? From what version were most of the Old Testament quotations in the New Testament taken? Why?
3) The Old Testament is incomplete. It closes leaving unexplained ceremonies (sacrificial rituals); unachieved commitments (the covenants); unappeased longings (poetical books); and, unfulfilled prophecies. Compile lists of the major ones in each category.

Session 13:

1) Compile a catalog of prophecies fulfilled in the New Testament.
2) Compile a catalog of prophecies that are *not yet* fulfilled in a) the Old Testament; and b) the New Testament.
3) Compare the results calculated with our simplified formula with those applying Bayes' Theorem.

Session 14:

1) Compile a time line showing the major milestones in the development of the English Bible.
2) Explore recent discoveries which tend to revise New Testament manuscript dates *earlier*: Carlton Thiede, *The Jesus Papyrus*, et al.
3) Compile a compendium of "microcodes" and "macrocodes" and explain their value in authentication of the Biblical text.

Session 15:

1) Sketch a map of Israel, with the principal events included as a composite of the Gospels, in chronological order.
2) Compare the 7 Kingdom Parables (Matthew 13) with the 7 Letters to 7 Churches (Rev 2 & 3).

Session 16:

1) Compile a list of the *illegal* features of the six trials of Christ.
2) List the details that would seem to indicate that the "Garden Tomb" in Jerusalem is, indeed, the actual tomb from which Christ was resurrected.
3) Which member of the Trinity was responsible for the resurrection? For the Creation? Justify your answer with Scripture references.

Session 17:

1) How do the events in Acts 8 impact the possibility that the Ark of the Covenant is presently being guarded in Ethiopia to present to the Messiah when He rules on Mt. Zion?
2) Was the Book of Acts ("Luke Volume 2") a companion part of the precedent trial documents required for Paul's appeal to Caesar? What are the suggestive evidences that seem to support this conjecture?

Session 18:

1) Summarize the principal arguments between Calvinism and Arminianism. How should this be resolved?
2) What three epistles constitute a trilogy on Habakkuk 2:4? What does this imply regarding authorship? What was its impact on the Reformation?

Session 19:

1) Pick two epistles and investigate their historical background, principal message(s), and their practical impact for the Christian today.
2) Compare the 7 Kingdom Parables (Matthew 13) with the 7 Letters to 7 Churches (Rev 2 & 3) and the 7 churches that Paul wrote to. Is there a deliberate pattern in all three groups? If so, what is its significance?

Session 20:

1) Pick two epistles and investigate their historical background, principal message(s), and their practical impact for the Christian today.
2) Who wrote the Epistle to the Hebrews? Justify your answer. Why was it *not* signed?

Session 21:

1) Are there hints of the *harpazo* in the Old Testament? If so, where? If not, why not?
2) Compile the various arguments for and against the Pre-tribulation and Post-tribulation views.
3) Explore the historical evidences for the pre-tribulation views among the early church.
4) Examine the various arguments for and against Rosenthal's "Pre-Wrath" view.

Session 22:

1) Profile and compare the letters to the seven churches with: a) the 7 Kingdom Parables of Matthew 13; and b) the 7 churches that Paul wrote to; and c) the 7 pastors that Paul wrote to. If there is an evident design, what are the implications?
2) Compile a list of allusions (and identities) from both the Old Testament and the New Testa ment encountered in these chapters.

Session 23:

1) Compile a list of attributes and references to the "Antichrist."
2) Write a paper addressing one of the following questions: Why are the thrones, but not the 24 Elders, visible in Daniel 7? Are the Seals, Thunders, and Bowls all sequential or is there some parallelism suggested? Why are the Seven Thunders *not* recorded in Chapter 10?

Session 24:

1) How can this study be improved? What supplemental helps could be added?
2) Organize a home study fellowship in your neighborhood, professional group, or among your other personal associations.

What Is Koinonia Institute?

Koinonia Institute is dedicated to training and equipping the serious Christian to sojourn in today's world.

For several decades the ministry of Koinonia House has been to create, develop, and distribute educational materials for those who take the Bible seriously as the inerrant Word of God. As an affiliated ministry, the Koinonia Institute is focused on three supporting areas:

1) To provide instructional programs to facilitate serious study of the Bible among thinking Christians;
2) To encourage and facilitate both individual and small group weekly study programs for personal growth; and
3) To research, monitor and publish information to stimulate awareness of the strategic trends that impact our times and our personal ministries and stewardships.

The Institute is committed to accomplishing these goals through a program of lifelong learning—exploiting the Internet—and the creation and development of an intelligence network among its members.

The programs at the Koinonia Institute are organized around three "tracks"—avenues of study—which are concurrent paths of achievement: 1) The Berean Track; 2) The Issachar Track; and 3) The Koinonos Track. It is the objective of the Institute to encourage the student through a *balanced* program of simultaneous progress along *each* of these tracks. (Think of them as three legs on a stool: balance is an essential requisite for effectiveness.)

The **Berean Track** is the primary backbone of the Institute, motivated by the diligence of the Bereans: *These were more noble than those in Thessalonica, in that they received the word with all readiness of mind, yet searched the Scriptures daily, to prove whether those things were so* (Acts 17:11). The program begins with a strategic overview of the entire Bible, with an emphasis on its integrity of design, its extraterrestrial origin, and its inerrancy in the original autographs. When the final Berean Level is achieved, the student will have studied all 66 books of the Bible, verse-by-verse, with in-depth expositional commentaries based on a commitment to the inerrancy of the Word of God.

The **Issachar Track** is motivated by the diligence of the Sons of Issachar: *And of the Sons of Issachar, which were men that had understanding of the times, to know what Israel ought to do;* (1 Chronicles 12:32). The study of the prophetic Scriptures often suffers from its enthusiasts as much as from its detractors, and the Institute's course of study is aimed at encouraging an in-depth understanding of God's plan of redemption and an awareness of the times—and challenges—we currently face. One of the principal activities of the Institute is to monitor the strategic trends on our horizon and their relationship to the Biblical scenario that we are admonished to understand.

The **Koinonos Track** takes its imperative from the Third Commandment: *Thou shalt not take the name of the LORD thy God in vain; for the LORD will not hold him guiltless that taketh His name in vain* (Exodus 20:7). Κοινωνός *koinonos,* is the Greek word for a partner or participant; it also implies a fiduciary—one who puts his partner's interests ahead of his own. The Koinonos Track is intended to emphasize being a *doer* of the Word, not a hearer only. The Koinonos Track focuses on discipleship, servanthood, and ambassadorship. It also strongly encourages participation in a small study group as one of the most effective means of personal growth.

For additional information, please download our KI Handbook at www.studycenter.com